11+ Verbal Reasoning
Comprehension
For the **CEM** test

Comprehension questions are a seriously tricky part of the CEM 11+, so we've made a whole book of 10-Minute Tests to help children master them!

Each test is packed with realistic CEM-style questions, with detailed answers included in a pull-out booklet. There's even a progress chart to keep track of children's scores.

This is Book 1. You'll find more practice at the same difficulty level in Book 2!

10-Minute Tests

Ages
10-11

How to access your free Online Edition

This book includes a free Online Edition to read on your PC, Mac or tablet.
You'll just need to go to **cgpbooks.co.uk/extras** and enter this code:

0150 9895 4227 8163

By the way, this code only works for one person. If somebody else has used this book before you, they might have already claimed the Online Edition.

How to use this book

This book is made up of 10-minute tests and puzzle pages.
There are answers and detailed explanations in the pull-out section at the back of the book.

10-Minute Tests

- There are 31 tests in this book, each containing 12 questions.

- Each test is designed to target the type of comprehension questions that your child could come across in the verbal reasoning section of their 11+ test, and covers a variety of text types at the right difficulty level.

- Your child should aim to score around 10 or 11 out of 12 in each of the 10-minute tests.
  If they score less than this, use their results to work out the areas they need more practice on.

- If your child hasn't managed to finish the test in time, they need to work on increasing their speed, whereas if they have made a lot of mistakes, they need to work more carefully.

- Keep track of your child's scores using the progress chart on the inside back cover of the book.

Puzzle Pages

- There are 11 puzzle pages in this book, which are a great break from test-style questions. They encourage children to practise similar skills to those that they will need in the test, but in a fun way.

Published by CGP

Editors: Heather McClelland, Holly Poynton, Sean Walsh

With thanks to Claire Boulter and Alison Griffin for the proofreading.

With thanks to the Literary Trustees of Walter de la Mare and the Society of Authors as their representative for permission to reproduce the poem on page 46.

Please note that CGP is not associated with CEM in any way.
This book does not include any official questions and is not endorsed by CEM.

ISBN: 978 1 78908 190 9
Printed by Elanders Ltd, Newcastle upon Tyne
Clipart from Corel®

Based on the classic CGP style created by Richard Parsons.

Contents

You have **10 minutes** to do this test. Work as quickly and accurately as you can.

Read this passage carefully and answer the questions that follow.

An extract from 'Great Expectations'

My father's family name being Pirrip, and my Christian name Philip, my infant
tongue could make of both names nothing longer or more explicit than Pip. So, I
called myself Pip, and came to be called Pip.

I give Pirrip as my father's family name, on the authority of his tombstone and my
5 sister — Mrs. Joe Gargery, who married the blacksmith. As I never saw my father or
my mother, and never saw any likeness of either of them (for their days were long
before the days of photographs), my first fancies regarding what they were like were
unreasonably derived from their tombstones. The shape of the letters on my father's,
gave me an odd idea that he was a square, stout, dark man, with curly black hair.

10 From the character and turn of the inscription, *"Also Georgiana Wife of the Above,"*
I drew a childish conclusion that my mother was freckled and sickly. To five little
stone lozenges*, each about a foot and a half long, which were arranged in a neat
row beside their grave, and were sacred to the memory of five little brothers of mine
— who gave up trying to get a living, exceedingly early in that universal struggle — I
15 am indebted for a belief I religiously entertained that they had all been born on their
backs with their hands in their trousers-pockets, and had never taken them out in
this state of existence.

Ours was the marsh country, down by the river, within, as the river wound, twenty
miles of the sea. My first most vivid and broad impression of the identity of things
20 seems to me to have been gained on a memorable raw afternoon towards evening.
At such a time I found out for certain that this bleak place overgrown with nettles
was the churchyard.

Charles Dickens

* stone lozenges — *diamond-shaped stones*

Answer these questions about the text that you've just read.
Circle the letter that matches the correct answer.

1. According to the text, why is the narrator called Pip?

   (A) As a child, he couldn't pronounce his full name.

   B His parents shortened his full name.

   C He was small, like a seed.

   D He wanted to be known by the name Pip.

2. What is Pip's full name?

   A Pirrip Philip

   (B) Philip Pirrip

   C Pip Pirrip

   D Philip Pip

3. Pip gives his surname on the "authority" (line 4) of his father's tombstone. This means:

   A he swears on his father's grave it's his surname.

   B he believes the inscription on his father's tombstone must be correct.

   C he promised his deceased father he would never lie about his surname.

   (D) Pip inherited his surname when his father died.

4. Which of the following best describes what Pip's father looked like?

   A Muscular and dark-haired

   B Slender with curly hair

   C Short with dark features

   (D) It is not clear from the text

TURN OVER ➡

5. What relation is Georgiana to Pip?

    A   His mother

    B   His sister

    C   His wife

    D   His grandmother

6. According to the text, Pip believed that his mother was "freckled and sickly" (line 11) because:

    A   his sister told him what his mother looked like.

    B   the style of the tombstone inscription is speckled and thin.

    C   he remembers seeing a photograph of his mother.

    D   the tombstone describes her as freckled and sickly.

7. What does Pip mean by the "universal struggle" (line 14)?

    A   A struggle to understand the universe.

    B   A struggle across the universe.

    C   Something only a few people have to experience.

    D   A common struggle that everyone experiences.

8. Which of the following statements must be false?

    A   Pip's parents had at least seven children.

    B   Pip is an orphan.

    C   Pip is the last surviving member of his family.

    D   Pip's father died when Pip was very young.

9. What information is not given in the passage?

A   Pip's brother-in-law's occupation

B   Pip's sister's surname

C   Pip's father's first name

D   The number of Pip's brothers buried in the churchyard

10. Pip "religiously entertained" (line 15) a belief. This means that Pip:

A   found the belief funny and entertaining.

B   thought about the belief constantly and without question.

C   held a very particular belief about religion.

D   tried to avoid thinking about the belief.

11. What does "raw" (line 20) mean?

A   Cold

B   Bright

C   Dark

D   Misty

12. What does "bleak" (line 21) mean?

A   Uninhabited

B   Fallow

C   Emptiness

D   Desolate

END OF TEST

/ 12

You have **10 minutes** to do this test. Work as quickly and accurately as you can.

Read this passage carefully and answer the questions that follow.

Inspector Cross

Inspector Cross walked down the cold, dark street, illuminated only by street lamps and the flashing neon sign of a corner shop. He was about to clock off when he received the call — another burglary. The sleepy village of Lakesworth had been renowned for its low crime rate; there had only been three incidents in the
5   last five years. However, in the last six months there had been seven burglaries, all seemingly unconnected.

The increased workload was certainly enough to make Inspector Cross grumble more than usual. He had been in the force for most of his working life and was close to retirement. He had plans for a world cruise with his wife; lazy Monday
10   breakfasts on the patio; and he would finally have time to look after a dog.

However, Inspector Cross had other things on his mind. His stomach was grumbling more than he usually did, so he headed towards the neon sign. At night, the shop had a strange glow about it. It was as though the produce radiated light, making it strangely hypnotising.
15   Choosing an item, Cross paid and left. It had been ten minutes since he had received the call, and stepping from the luminous shop to the dark, empty street was like stepping back into a sad reality. Although the moon had appeared from behind a cloud, illuminating the street, the food looked ordinary without the bright lights of the shop.
20   Inspector Cross checked his phone. He had twenty minutes left until he had to be at the crime scene. He walked over to a bench on the far side of the street and sat down. Cross looked up at the moon and ate his sandwich, taking a brief pause from the intensity of his job to appreciate that life wasn't really all bad.

Answer these questions about the text that you've just read.
Circle the letter that matches the correct answer.

1. According to the text, which of the following statements is true?

   A   Lakesworth is a bustling and vibrant place.

   B   Cross was about to leave work when he received the call.

   C   The latest burglary had been committed in broad daylight.

   D   There had been 10 burglaries over the last 5 years.

2. According to the text, why are the recent burglaries strange?

   A   They all appear to have been committed by the same person.

   B   They all appear to have been committed by different people.

   C   There were no clues at the scene of the crime.

   D   They all happened simultaneously.

3. According to the passage, which of the following statements are true?

   1. Inspector Cross has worked as a policeman for a long time.
   2. There had only been three burglaries in Lakesworth in the past five years.
   3. Cross finds his job demanding at times.
   4. Inspector Cross is unmarried.

   A   1 and 2

   B   2 and 4

   C   2 and 3

   D   1 and 3

TURN OVER ➡

4. What reason is given in the text for Inspector Cross's grumpiness?

    A   The flickering neon sign

    B   His feeling of hunger

    C   The changing amount of work since the burglaries

    D   The cold weather

5. According to the text, how is Inspector Cross planning to spend his retirement?

    A   Going on a cruise, reading the Monday newspaper and getting a cat.

    B   Meeting old friends, travelling with his wife and getting a dog.

    C   Getting a pet, travelling the world and reading novels.

    D   Relaxed mornings, getting a pet and spending time with his wife.

6. Why does Inspector Cross walk over to the shop?

    A   He is hypnotised by the neon sign.

    B   He is hungry.

    C   He is distracted.

    D   He wants to get out of the cold.

7. "It was as though the produce radiated light" (line 13). What does this mean?

    A   The food contains harmful radiation.

    B   The food appears to absorb light.

    C   The food appears to give off its own light.

    D   The food is warm, like a radiator.

8. Why doesn't Inspector Cross see the moon at the start of the text?

    A   He is too distracted by the crime.

    B   He cannot see because of the bright street lamps.

    C   The moon is hidden behind a cloud.

    D   It is a moonless night.

9. How long after receiving the phone call does Inspector Cross have to arrive at the crime scene?

   A   10 minutes

   B   20 minutes

   C   30 minutes

   D   40 minutes

10. Which of the following statements best describes Cross's feelings in lines 21-23?

    A   He feels full after eating his sandwich.

    B   He feels calmed by the stillness of the moon.

    C   He feels that a brief pause is needed to eat his sandwich.

    D   He feels he should relax before walking further.

11. What does the word "renowned" (line 4) mean?

    A   Congratulated

    B   Infamous

    C   Named

    D   Well-known

12. What does the word "luminous" (line 16) mean?

    A   Bright

    B   Vivid

    C   Flashing

    D   Enlightening

END OF TEST

/ 12

Time for a break! These puzzles are a great way to sharpen your **vocabulary** skills.

Synonym Search

Complete the word search by finding and writing down a **synonym** for each of the words below.

huge _____

old _____

sad _____

pretty _____

right _corred_____

bad _evil_____

L	U	F	I	T	U	A	E	B	R	S
R	D	F	A	R	S	J	N	R	N	T
S	D	A	A	D	F	S	O	G	D	S
Y	U	H	D	D	S	A	R	D	S	F
A	N	C	I	E	N	T	M	E	D	B
F	H	S	O	I	J	S	O	F	S	Y
D	A	L	D	R	A	S	U	S	U	K
A	P	R	U	F	R	F	S	S	D	L
R	P	U	S	F	B	E	V	I	L	R
T	Y	J	R	A	F	B	C	E	T	S
R	A	H	P	I	A	E	L	T	J	A

Spelling Bee

Each word below is misspelt. First, cross out the wrong letters, then rearrange the wrong letters to reveal the bee's favourite flower.

D E P P A R T M E N T

I R R I T I B L E

A C C E P T A B L E

O C C U R R U N C E

P A S T T I M E

Bee's Favourite Flower: _tulip_____

You have **10 minutes** to do this test. Work as quickly and accurately as you can.

Read this passage carefully and answer the questions that follow.

The Tomato is Mightier than the Sword

In Buñol, a town in Valencia, Spain, a most unusual event takes place every year on the last Wednesday of August. La Tomatina is a festival where participants pelt each other with over one hundred metric tons of tomatoes in a friendly battle. The first Tomatina took place in 1945, but its origins remain mysterious. Some believe
5   it all began when a food fight broke out among friends. Others say that citizens attacked the town's councillors with tomatoes during a celebration.

Prior to 2013, between 30 000 to 50 000 people took part each year, but because the town struggled to accommodate so many guests, the annual headcount is limited to 20 000 people, and all participants must now have a ticket.

10   Before the chaos begins, shopkeepers batten down the hatches in preparation for the sea of red slush that swamps the town. At around 11 o'clock, a leg of ham is placed on a large, greased pole. No tomatoes should be thrown until somebody has climbed the pole and retrieved the ham. However, climbing the pole can be difficult (and sometimes unachievable), so the water cannon used to signal the start
15   of the festival is occasionally fired early. After an hour or so, the cannon fires again, at which point the tomato throwing stops.

For safety reasons, tomatoes should be squashed before throwing. No one is allowed to bring anything that could potentially injure another person, and it is not considered sporting to tear someone else's clothes. Revellers are also encouraged to
20   wear protective goggles and gloves.

After the food fight, fire trucks hose down the streets whilst portable showers or the Buñol River help people clean themselves off. Then, despite the fact that the event makes such a mess and squanders a vast amount of food, it all happens again in twelve months.

TURN OVER ➡

Answer these questions about the text that you've just read.
Circle the letter that matches the correct answer.

1. Where does the festival take place?

   A   In Buñol, a village in Tomatina

   B   In Tomatina, a city in Spain

   C   In Valencia, a region in Buñol

   D   In Buñol, a town in Spain

2. Which of these statements about the festival's origins must be false?

   A   The first Tomatina took place in the 1940s.

   B   The idea clearly came from a group of friends having a food fight.

   C   The reason why the festival took place for the first time is unknown.

   D   The festival may have been inspired by angry townsfolk.

3. According to the text, which of the following statements is true?

   A   The festival attracts more visitors each year.

   B   Concerns about overcrowding led to the festival becoming a ticketed event.

   C   Approximately 100 kg of tomatoes are thrown during the festival.

   D   Local residents resent the disruption caused by the festival.

4. According to the text, which of the following statements is false?

   A   There were more participants in 2013 than in 2012.

   B   There were more participants in 2011 than in 2014.

   C   In 2015, approximately 20 000 people took part.

   D   Over 30 000 people took part in 2011.

5. Shopkeepers "batten down the hatches" (line 10). What does this mean?

   A   Shopkeepers arm themselves ready for the battle.

   B   Shopkeepers try to protect their property.

   C   Shopkeepers often sell out of tomatoes during the festival.

   D   Shopkeepers complain about the damage caused during the festival.

6. What is the "sea of red slush" (line 11)?

   A   Liquid fired from the water cannon

   B   Overflowing water from the portable showers

   C   The squashed tomatoes thrown by the visitors

   D   Blood from the injuries suffered during the food fight

7. What signals the start of the food fight?

   A   A leg of ham being taken from a large pole

   B   A cannon firing

   C   When an official throws a tomato

   D   When someone climbs to the top of a greased pole

8. According to the passage, how does the food fight end?

   A   A ceasefire is signalled by a cannon firing for a second time.

   B   When the fire trucks arrive

   C   Once the cannon has been fired three times, tomato throwing stops.

   D   Recovering a leg of ham from the top of a pole marks the end of the festival.

TURN OVER ➡

9. What measure is taken to keep people safe during the festival?

  A   Tomato growers only supply squashed tomatoes.

  B   The fighting is limited to roughly 60 minutes.

  C   Items that could harm others are prohibited.

  D   Fire engines patrol the streets.

10. Which of the following statements is not mentioned in the passage?

  A   Fire trucks wash away tomatoes after the festival ends.

  B   Revellers are provided with protective goggles and gloves.

  C   Tomato throwing lasts for an hour or so.

  D   The festival takes place on the last Wednesday of the 8th month.

11. The author says the event "squanders a vast amount of food" (line 23). What does this mean?

  A   Food that would otherwise be wasted is put to good use.

  B   Visitors consume huge amounts of food whilst in Buñol.

  C   A lot of tomatoes are wasted during the festival.

  D   Participants are not restricted to just throwing tomatoes.

12. What does the word "Revellers" (line 19) mean?

  A   People who celebrate an event

  B   People who spectate an event

  C   People who ensure the safety of the crowd

  D   People who are likely to get hurt

END OF TEST

/ 12

You have **10 minutes** to do this test. Work as quickly and accurately as you can.

Read this passage carefully and answer the questions that follow.

The Boat and the Boy

I float atop an empty sunlit lake,
my boat in precious gold reflected.
Long rays of light fall on my face,
on skin which shade so long neglected.
5 My young son keenly looks for fish;
far from the light's great fiery glow,
they hide in dark and cooler waters,
moving down to the depths below.

Slowly reaching the water's edge,
10 down the burning orb goes.
It spreads out its arms;
it dips in its toes.
Submerging its body,
right up to its head,
15 the orange light changes
to a dark shade of red.

The once golden surface
is furiously set ablaze.
My son touches the water,
20 it ripples and plays.
The light dances round,
like a skater on ice,
but it's almost gone now,
the day's last sacrifice.

25 Tiredness creeps on his lids,
my son's eyes start to close.
The water turns purple,
and the waking moon grows.
Peeking out from the clouds,
30 once so golden and bright;
turned wan by the moon,
the clouds signal the night.

Eventually the stars appear;
my son lays down his head.
35 They light up the water,
now silver instead.
My boat still reflected,
in water so slow,
remains just as precious,
40 but my son is more so.

TURN OVER ➡

Answer these questions about the text that you've just read.
Circle the letter that matches the correct answer.

1. The narrator says that the sunlight falls "on skin which shade so long neglected" (line 4). This tell us that:

    A   the narrator spends a lot of time indoors.

    B   the narrator spends a lot of time outdoors.

    C   the sunlight casts shadows across the narrator's face.

    D   the narrator neglects his appearance.

2. Why does the boy struggle to see the fish?

    A   The sun has set, so it is too dark to see them.

    B   He cannot see because of the reflection on the water.

    C   The fish move too quickly.

    D   The fish are at the bottom of the lake.

3. Which of the following best describes the sunset?

    A   It is as though the sun goes directly into the water.

    B   It makes the water appear red and then orange.

    C   The shadows cast by the sunset resemble a human figure.

    D   It is beautiful, but sudden.

4. Which of the following cannot be true?

    A   The stars come out after the moon.

    B   The man has been on the lake all day.

    C   There are other boats on the lake.

    D   The young son is hungry for fish.

5. In the poem, which of the following events occur at the same time?
   1. The moon appears from behind a cloud.
   2. The sunset is reflected on the lake.
   3. The boy touches the water.
   4. The boy falls asleep.

   A   1 and 2
   B   2 and 4
   C   2 and 3
   D   1 and 3

6. Which of the following is described as "the day's last sacrifice" (line 24)?
   A   The ripples on the lake
   B   The sunlight
   C   The boy
   D   The reflection in the water

7. Which of the following words isn't used to describe the colour of the water?
   A   Gold
   B   Orange
   C   Purple
   D   Silver

8. According to the poem, which of the following statements must be true?
   A   The water on the lake is choppy.
   B   The boat is painted silver.
   C   The boy is awake when the moon comes out.
   D   It becomes impossible to see when the sun sets.

TURN OVER ➡

9. The "golden surface" (line 17) refers to:

    A   the side of the boat.

    B   a jetty on the lake.

    C   the surface of the sun.

    D   the surface of the water.

10. Which of the following is the boy as precious as?

    A   A precious metal

    B   The boat

    C   Water

    D   None of the above

11. What does "Submerging" (line 13) mean?

    A   Shrouding

    B   Immersing

    C   Hiding

    D   Soaking

12. What does "wan" (line 31) mean?

    A   Mysterious

    B   Gloomy

    C   Wispy

    D   Pale

END OF TEST

/ 12

Time for a break! These puzzles are a great way to practise your **word-making** skills.

Compound-Word Chain

Use the twelve puzzle pieces below to create eight compound words.

The first one has been done for you.

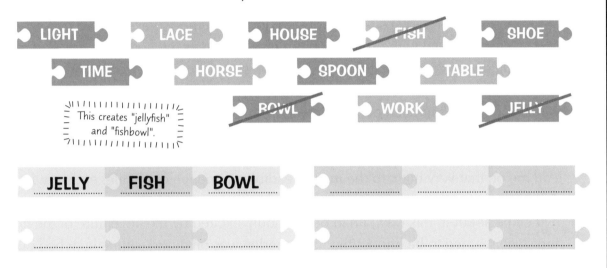

This creates "jellyfish" and "fishbowl".

JELLY FISH BOWL

Anagram Anacondas

Anagram anacondas are well known for their word-covered scales, but the words can become jumbled.

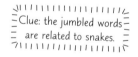

Clue: the jumbled words are related to snakes.

Help these snakes rearrange their letters so that they display their original word.

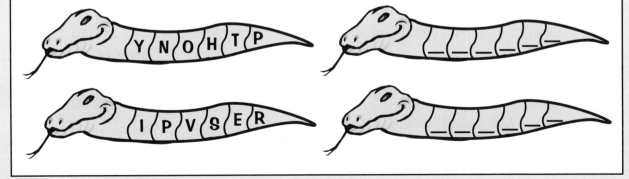

You have **10 minutes** to do this test. Work as quickly and accurately as you can.

> Read this passage carefully and answer the questions that follow.

An extract from 'The Lost World'

I have said — or perhaps I have not said, for my memory plays me sad tricks these days — that I glowed with pride when three such men as my comrades thanked me for having saved, or at least greatly helped, the situation. As the youngster of the party, not merely in years, but in experience, character, knowledge, and all that goes
5   to make a man, I had been overshadowed from the first. And now I was coming into my own. I warmed at the thought. Alas! for the pride which goes before a fall! That little glow of self-satisfaction, that added measure of self-confidence, were to lead me on that very night to the most dreadful experience of my life, ending with a shock which turns my heart sick when I think of it.
10   It came about in this way. I had been unduly excited by the adventure of the tree, and sleep seemed to be impossible. Summerlee was on guard, sitting hunched over our small fire, a quaint, angular figure, his rifle across his knees and his pointed, goat-like beard wagging with each weary nod of his head. Lord John lay silent, wrapped in the South American poncho* which he wore, while Challenger snored
15 with a roll and rattle which reverberated through the woods. The full moon was shining brightly, and the air was crisply cold. What a night for a walk! And then suddenly came the thought, "Why not?" Suppose I stole softly away, suppose I made my way down to the central lake, suppose I was back at breakfast with some record of the place — would I not in that case be thought an even more worthy associate?
20 Then, if Summerlee carried the day** and some means of escape were found, we should return to London with first-hand knowledge of the central mystery of the plateau***, to which I alone, of all men, would have penetrated****.

Arthur Conan Doyle

* poncho — *a large piece of cloth with a hole in the middle for your head*
** carried the day — *was successful*
*** plateau — *a high, large, flat area of land*
**** penetrated — *had access to*

Answer these questions about the text that you've just read.
Circle the letter that matches the correct answer.

1. The narrator says "my memory plays me sad tricks these days" (lines 1-2). This tells us that:

    A   he is trying to forget about what happened to him.

    B   his memory isn't as good as it used to be.

    C   he is trying to remember an event from a long time ago.

    D   the events he's remembering make him feel emotional.

2. According to the extract, what makes the narrator stand out from the other men on the expedition?

    A   He is the proudest.

    B   He is the most excitable.

    C   He is the youngest.

    D   He is the only one not wearing a poncho.

3. Which of the following is not mentioned as one of the things that make up a man?

    A   Character

    B   Knowledge

    C   Experience

    D   Self-confidence

4. What does the narrator mean when he says "I warmed at the thought" (line 6)?

    A   The thought makes him feel embarrassed.

    B   The thought makes him feel proud.

    C   The thought makes him feel nervous.

    D   The thought makes him feel excited.

TURN OVER ➡

5. What does the narrator mean by "the pride which goes before a fall" (line 6)?

   A   He tripped after feeling happy about his achievement.

   B   He knew he was about to take a risk, but he felt confident.

   C   He was overly confident, and something bad happened to him because of it.

   D   He was pleased with himself and felt glad.

6. According to the extract, why is the narrator unable to sleep?

   A   He is too exhilarated after a previous event.

   B   He is too distracted by Challenger's snoring.

   C   He is too nervous about the day ahead.

   D   He is eager to go to the central lake.

7. Which of the following statements about Summerlee is false?

   A   He is wearing a poncho.

   B   He is bony.

   C   He has a rifle.

   D   He has a beard.

8. Which of the following best describes the evening?

   A   It is a crisp, quiet night.

   B   It is a cold, moonlit night.

   C   It is a warm, wet night.

   D   It is a dry, warm night.

9. Which of the following best describes what the narrator hopes to achieve when he decides to go for a walk?

   A   That he will return with a clearer head.

   B   That he will make it back in time for breakfast.

   C   That he will walk past the furthest lake.

   D   That he will return with information that will impress the others.

10. Which best describes the narrator of the extract?

   A   He is brave but cautious.

   B   He is young and impulsive.

   C   He is arrogant and boastful.

   D   He is unappreciated and shy.

11. What does "stole" (line 17) mean in the context of the passage?

   A   To leave quietly without being seen.

   B   To take something and leave quickly.

   C   To run away as fast as possible.

   D   To escape with something you shouldn't.

12. What does "associate" (line 19) mean?

   A   Man

   B   Companion

   C   Explorer

   D   Pioneer

END OF TEST

/ 12

You have **10 minutes** to do this test. Work as quickly and accurately as you can.

Read this passage carefully and answer the questions that follow.

Timbuktu

A person who is about to make a long journey to a distant location might exclaim, "I'm off to Timbuktu!" It is the remoteness of Timbuktu, a city in the Republic of Mali, a West African country, which inspires this comparison. Even with today's transport links, it takes approximately fourteen hours to travel by car from
5 Bamako, Mali's capital, to the southern edge of the Sahara Desert, where Timbuktu is situated.

It is believed that Timbuktu was settled around the 11th century by the Tuareg people, as its location near the Niger River provided water and grazing land for their livestock. Over the centuries this settlement grew, and became home to other tribes
10 of people, such as the Fulani and Songhai. Timbuktu eventually became a centre of trade, thanks in part to the Niger River, which was used for transporting goods. From the fourteenth century, the trade in salt, ivory and gold was thriving.

The city also became a hive of intellectual activity which was partly due to the number of manuscripts which were imported to Timbuktu. Whilst on their way back
15 from pilgrimages to Mecca, Timbuktu's scholars sometimes copied texts in Egypt, which they would then take back to their own libraries.

Personal libraries were prevalent among Timbuktu's scholarly elite. One such intellectual, Ahmed Baba (1556-1627), owned a library which contained over 1600 books. But even this seemingly sizable assortment was considered small in
20 comparison to other personal libraries.

In 1973, the Ahmed Baba Institute of Higher Learning and Islamic Research, a library and research centre, was named in honour of Baba.

Answer these questions about the text that you've just read.
Circle the letter that matches the correct answer.

1. According to the text, why is it inappropriate to compare Timbuktu to a town that is quick to get to?

    A   There are limited routes into and out of Timbuktu.

    B   Timbuktu is very isolated.

    C   Timbuktu can only be reached by boat.

    D   It is impossible to estimate how long it will take to get to Timbuktu.

2. According to the text, which of the following must be true?

    A   West Africa is a country.

    B   West Africa is isolated.

    C   Mali is a city.

    D   Timbuktu is in Africa.

3. Where is the Sahara Desert located in relation to Timbuktu?

    A   To the south

    B   To the east

    C   To the north

    D   To the west

4. Which of the following made Timbuktu attractive to the first settlers?

    A   Its remote location

    B   The Niger River

    C   The possibility of finding gold

    D   Its proximity to Bamako

TURN OVER ➡

5. According to the text, which of the following statements must be true?

   A   Cargo was shipped along the Niger River.

   B   The Songhai people travelled to Timbuktu to look for gold.

   C   The Fulani people brought salt to Timbuktu.

   D   The Fulani people grazed their livestock on the banks of the River Niger.

6. Which of the following words describes the salt trade in Timbuktu during the 1300s?

   A   Dwindling

   B   Illegal

   C   Tumultuous

   D   Flourishing

7. The author says that Timbuktu was "a hive of intellectual activity" (line 13). What does this mean?

   A   A dangerous place for scholars

   B   A busy and important place of learning

   C   A disorganised educational environment

   D   A secluded haven for intellectuals

8. Which of the following describes the manuscripts that were brought to Timbuktu?

   A   Religious

   B   Valuable

   C   Foreign

   D   Stolen

9. Who was most likely to have a personal library in Timbuktu?

    A   Pilgrims

    B   Egyptians

    C   Tribesmen

    D   Traders

10. Which of the following statements cannot be true?

    A   Ahmed Baba owned the smallest collection of books in Timbuktu.

    B   Reading was a popular pastime in Timbuktu.

    C   Ahmed Baba died at the age of seventy-one.

    D   All inhabitants of Timbuktu had their own library.

11. According to the text, why was an organisation named after Ahmed Baba?

    A   Because it was the 350th anniversary of his death

    B   Because he owned 1600 books

    C   Because he contributed to its library

    D   Because it was a sign of respect

12. What does "prevalent" (line 17) mean?

    A   Precious

    B   Widespread

    C   Established

    D   Accepted

END OF TEST

/ 12

You have **10 minutes** to do this test. Work as quickly and accurately as you can.

Read this passage carefully and answer the questions that follow.

An abridged extract from 'Peter Pan'

Mrs. Darling loved to have everything just so, and Mr. Darling had a passion for being exactly like his neighbours; so, of course, they had a nurse*. As they were poor, owing to the amount of milk the children drank, this nurse was a prim Newfoundland dog, called Nana, who had belonged to no one in particular until
5 the Darlings engaged her. She had always thought children important, however, and the Darlings had become acquainted with her in Kensington Gardens, where she spent most of her spare time peeping into perambulators**, and was much hated by careless nursemaids, whom she followed to their homes and complained of to their mistresses. She proved to be quite a treasure of a nurse. How thorough she
10 was at bath-time, and up at any moment of the night if one of her charges made the slightest cry. Of course her kennel was in the nursery. She had a genius for knowing when a cough is a thing to have no patience with and when it needs stocking*** around your throat. She believed to her last day in old-fashioned remedies like rhubarb leaf, and made sounds of contempt**** over all this new-fangled talk about
15 germs, and so on. It was a lesson in propriety***** to see her escorting the children to school, walking sedately by their side when they were well behaved, and butting them back into line if they strayed. On John's footer [in England soccer was called football, "footer" for short] days she never once forgot his sweater, and she usually carried an umbrella in her mouth in case of rain.
20 No nursery could possibly have been conducted more correctly, and Mr. Darling knew it, yet he sometimes wondered uneasily whether the neighbours talked.
He had his position in the city to consider.

J. M. Barrie

* nurse — *nanny*
** perambulators — *prams*
*** stocking — *covering*
**** contempt — *disapproval*
***** propriety — *socially acceptable behaviour*

Answer these questions about the text that you've just read.
Circle the letter that matches the correct answer.

1. Which of the words below best describes Mrs. Darling?

    A   Exacting

    B   Determined

    C   Vague

    D   Confident

2. According to the passage, why do the Darling family have a nurse?

    A   Because they have three children

    B   Because their neighbours have nurses

    C   Because Mr. Darling works in the city

    D   Because the children need taking to school

3. Why do the Darling family have a dog as a nurse?

    A   They could not afford a human nurse.

    B   They wanted to be different.

    C   They believed human nursemaids were careless.

    D   They believed nobody could look after the nursery better.

4. According to the text, why aren't the Darlings wealthy?

    A   Mr. Darling spends too much money trying to impress the neighbours.

    B   Mr. Darling's position in the city isn't well paid.

    C   Running the household is expensive.

    D   The family spends a lot of money on milk.

TURN OVER ➡

5. Which of the following best describes Nana?

    A   She is loved by the children.

    B   She is accepted by other nursemaids.

    C   She has a relaxed approach to childcare.

    D   She is very competent.

6. Who does "charges" (line 10) refer to?

    A   Nana's puppies

    B   Other nursemaids

    C   The Darling children

    D   Mr. and Mrs. Darling

7. The author tells us that Nana knows "when a cough is a thing to have no patience with" (line 12). This tells us that:

    A   Nana is irritated by the sound of coughing.

    B   Nana is always careful to look after the children when they're ill.

    C   Nana can tell when the children are faking an illness.

    D   The children are often unwell.

8. According to the passage, where does Nana sleep?

    A   In the same room as the children

    B   In her own room

    C   In a kennel in Kensington Gardens

    D   In a kennel outside

9. What does Nana's role as a nurse include?

   A   Bathing the children

   B   Taking the children to school

   C   Looking after the children when they are sick

   D   All of the above

10. According to the text, Mr. Darling worries that the neighbours:

   A   disapprove of the Darling family's choice of nurse.

   B   disapprove of his work in the city.

   C   disapprove of how the nursery is conducted.

   D   disapprove of Nana's complaints about careless nursemaids.

11. What does "engaged her" (line 5) mean?

   A   Paid her attention

   B   Hired her

   C   Gave her a name

   D   Disagreed with her

12. What does "sedately" (line 16) mean?

   A   Solemnly

   B   Strictly

   C   Calmly

   D   Carefully

END OF TEST

/ 12

Time for a break! This puzzle is a great way to practise your **vocabulary** skills.

The Adverb Crossword

Complete the crossword by choosing an appropriate **adverb** to complete each of the sentences below.

ACROSS

4   David _____ had his third slice of cake.

7   Gemma knocked the vase over _____.

8   Peter _____ didn't know who broke the window.

9   Nicola _____ tiptoed downstairs to the fridge.

10 James ran _____ over to the bouncy castle.

DOWN

1   Jennifer smiled _____.

2   Mark _____ shoved his lunchbox into his bag.

3   Lucy waited _____ for the next bus.

5   Geoff _____ picked up the broken photo frame.

6   Sandra drove her car _____ fast around the corner.

You have **10 minutes** to do this test. Work as quickly and accurately as you can.

Read this passage carefully and answer the questions that follow.

Writer's Block

It has been said that a poorly skilled writer trying to write a novel is like a builder trying to build a house with cardboard and glue: it simply won't hold together. I only wish I could get as far as finishing a novel; whether it fell apart at the end or not, it would be an accomplishment. My parents always warned me against
5 becoming a writer: they said it wasn't a stable career, but I always felt that I was good enough to prove them wrong. However, considering my book is nonexistent, perhaps I am not always right.

The main issue I have is coming up with an idea good enough to sustain an entire novel. I take inspiration from people that I see going about their lives. Even people
10 walking the streets interest me: their individual quirks and little variations on the day-to-day activities of life show just how rich life is. Writers like Charles Dickens and Edgar Allan Poe are masters at this, turning the mundane into the fascinating.

Perhaps I don't have enough life experience to justify writing a novel. It is said that some of the best authors fictionalise their own personal experiences, and often
15 true stories are the most far-fetched. Just ask the biographer of any rock star!

I am often unsure, is it style or substance that makes a novel great? You could have a beautifully written novel about something utterly boring, or a poorly written novel about something incredible. The best-written stories are my favourites, but I'm not sure they fly off the shelves in the same way as books with a great plot. It seems
20 the best authors merge the two in a kind of alchemy, which is something I aspire to.

So here I sit, with my pen in hand and blank piece of paper staring at me. All I need to do is write something on the page; any string of words will do. The one thing I know is, I must prove my parents wrong, whatever the cost.

TURN OVER ➡

Answer these questions about the text that you've just read.
Circle the letter that matches the correct answer.

1. Which of the following does the writer compare writing a novel to?

   A   A fine art

   B   A tricky dilemma

   C   Being a master of the mundane

   D   Construction work   ✓

2. Which of the following best describes the current goal of the writer?

   A   To finish a novel regardless of the quality

   B   To write a book that merges style and substance

   C   To write a novel that will sell many copies

   D   To create a stable career for herself

3. Which of the words below best describes the writer's parents?

   A   Disrespectful

   B   Practical

   C   Indifferent

   D   Sympathetic

4. What reason does the author give for being unable to prove her parents wrong?

   A   Her book isn't very good.

   B   She hasn't written a book.

   C   Her parents don't like her book.

   D   Her book hasn't sold many copies.

5. According to the passage, which of the following does the writer use for inspiration?

   A   The novelists she grew up reading

   B   The little differences seen in every human being

   C   The pressure her parents put on her

   D   The biographies of rock stars

6. According to the passage, what does the writer admire about Charles Dickens?

   A   The way he could create such interesting descriptions

   B   How many ideas he could fit into one novel

   C   The way he could make anything appear interesting

   D   The way he could make any character engaging

7. The author thinks that the biographies of rock stars are:

   A   too far-fetched.

   B   not always based on personal experience.

   C   an exaggerated version of the truth.

   D   almost too outlandish to be believable.

8. According to the passage, which of the following statements is true?

   A   The writer doubts whether her ideas will fill a novel.

   B   The writer's parents are characters in her novel.

   C   The novel is about people's everyday lives.

   D   The novel follows the styles of Dickens and Poe.

TURN OVER ➡

9. What does the writer conclude about the best novels?

   A   They should have a great idea that lasts the entire novel.

   B   They should be beautifully written.

   C   They should have a solid structure that holds together.

   D   They should contain both style and substance.

10. According to the author, what type of book sells the most copies?

   A   Well-written books

   B   Books with realistic characters

   C   Books that have a good storyline

   D   Books that are both well written and have a good plot

11. What does "sustain" (line 8) mean?

   A   Support

   B   Shorten

   C   Endorse

   D   Interest

12. What does "alchemy" (line 20) mean?

   A   A method of increasing the quality of a story

   B   A physical blending of objects

   C   An author's ability to create an original novel

   D   The process of changing something basic into an object of value

END OF TEST

/ 12

You have **10 minutes** to do this test. Work as quickly and accurately as you can.

Read this passage carefully and answer the questions that follow.

Coffee — Bean Around the World

Coffee drinkers around the globe consume around two billion cups each day, so it's not surprising that coffee is big business. Brazil is far and away the world leader when it comes to the quantity of coffee produced, and although it's the USA that imports the most coffee, Finland often tops the list as the country that drinks the
5 most coffee per capita. Most coffee lovers just need to add some hot water (and maybe a splash of milk or a bit of sugar) to make the perfect brew, but coffee beans have to go through a lot before they reach a cup!

The coffee bean isn't actually a bean — it's a seed which is found inside a berry. Each berry usually contains two seeds, and takes about nine months to ripen. In
10 around 5% of cases, only one seed develops — this lone seed is called a peaberry. Some coffee connoisseurs claim that coffee made from peaberries has a superior flavour, but for others, the jury's still out.

Processing the berries can be done in two ways — one dry, one wet. In the dry method, the berries are left to dry outside for up to four weeks, or until they reach
15 12% water content. This method is favoured in drier countries. The wet method requires machinery to pulp, ferment and wash the berries.

At this stage, the coffee is called "green coffee" because it hasn't been roasted, and it's the roasting process which gives the beans their distinctive dark brown appearance. During the roasting process, the beans are kept in constant motion to
20 avoid scorching as they are exposed to temperatures of approximately 220°C.

Finally, the coffee beans are ground up. The time it takes to brew the coffee depends on how fine or coarse the coffee grounds are. Coarser grounds generally take longer to brew than finer grounds, and both take longer than instant coffee.

TURN OVER ➡

Answer these questions about the text that you've just read.
Circle the letter that matches the correct answer.

1. According to the text, why is coffee "big business" (line 2)?

   A   Producing coffee is profitable because it happens overseas.

   B   Producing coffee is profitable because it is cheap to harvest.

   C   Producing coffee is profitable because so many people drink it.

   D   Producing coffee is profitable because it is cheap to import.

2. According to the text, which of the following best describes Brazil?

   A   Brazil produces the most coffee.

   B   Brazil produces the best coffee.

   C   Brazil exports the most coffee.

   D   Brazil is the authority on coffee production.

3. Which of the following statements must be true?

   A   Americans drink more coffee per person than any other country.

   B   Brazil imports more coffee than Finland.

   C   Finland imports more coffee than any other country.

   D   Finland imports less coffee than America.

4. Which of the following statements must be true?

   A   A peaberry is found inside a berry.

   B   Coffee seeds are found within a peaberry.

   C   A coffee bean contains a berry.

   D   Peaberries contain berry seeds.

5. According to the passage, for some coffee drinkers the "jury's still out" (line 12) on the flavour of peaberry coffee. This means that:

    A   they don't like peaberry coffee as much as regular coffee.

    B   they think peaberry coffee tastes better than regular coffee.

    C   they don't know enough about peaberry coffee.

    D   they haven't decided whether they prefer regular coffee or peaberry coffee.

6. Why are drier countries better suited to the dry method of processing coffee?

    A   If the berries are too wet they will develop only one seed.

    B   The berries need to reach a high temperature to develop.

    C   The berries are cleaned by people who require a dry environment.

    D   The berries are left to dry outside and so require dry heat.

7. According to the text, how is the wet method of coffee production different to the dry method?

    A   It requires more equipment.

    B   It is more profitable.

    C   It is less efficient.

    D   It produces superior coffee.

8. According to the passage, why are coffee beans sometimes kept moving?

    A   To speed up the dry method to less than 4 weeks

    B   To stop the beans from burning

    C   To make sure the shipment of coffee arrives in time

    D   To make sure the entire bean is washed properly

TURN OVER ➡

9. According to the passage, which type of coffee takes the shortest time to brew?

    A   Green coffee

    B   Coarse coffee grounds

    C   Fine coffee grounds

    D   Instant coffee

10. Which of the following is not mentioned in the passage?

    A   How the coffee bean develops a dark brown colour.

    B   Which method of processing gives the most flavour.

    C   The length of time it takes for a berry to ripen.

    D   The proportion of berries that contain a peaberry seed.

11. What does "connoisseurs" (line 11) mean?

    A   Experts

    B   Evaluators

    C   Analysts

    D   Inspectors

12. What does "distinctive" (line 18) mean?

    A   Strange

    B   Superior

    C   Peculiar

    D   Recognisable

END OF TEST

/ 12

You have **10 minutes** to do this test. Work as quickly and accurately as you can.

Read this passage carefully and answer the questions that follow.

Train of Thought

Trees — a quaint sweet shop — an elderly couple picnicking by a stream.
The scenery flew past so rapidly that Brian could only glimpse each image for a
moment. Living in a city, Brian was fascinated by the view from his window — as
he travelled further north, the uniform grey tower blocks and the congested roads
5 were replaced with dense woodland, rolling hills and sleepy villages.
Brian was visiting his friend, Lucy, who had moved to a village near the Yorkshire
Dales a couple of months ago. As a reformed city slicker, rural life had taken Lucy
some getting used to. She'd swapped extravagant shopping trips and gourmet
restaurants for countryside rambles and cosy nights indoors, and at first, Lucy had
10 thought her relocation had been a mistake. But as winter turned into spring, Lucy
had delighted at the blossoming trees, the woolly lambs and, above all, the country
air. She was also glad to be away from the hustle and bustle of tourists, and the
crammed underground trains.
Although Brian was pleased that his friend was growing accustomed to the
15 change of pace, he privately thought that rural life was no match for city living.
Still, he welcomed his weekend away with Lucy — life in the city was vibrant and
exciting, but it could also be exhausting.
Brian glanced at the holdall that was stowed in the rack above his seat. He
hoped that the sturdy trainers and parka he'd packed would meet with Lucy's
20 approval — the pair had planned to go walking and Lucy had insisted that Brian
pack appropriately. Apparently, there had been an incident last week when Lucy's
parents had paid a visit and had been caught out on the dales with nothing but a
flimsy cagoule and a broken umbrella.

TURN OVER ➡

Answer these questions about the text that you've just read.
Circle the letter that matches the correct answer.

1. Which of the following best describes the sweet shop?

    A   It is charming and old-fashioned.

    B   It is large and busy.

    C   It is part of a chain.

    D   It has been closed down.

2. According to the text, which of the following has Brian not seen on his journey?

    A   A stream

    B   Traffic

    C   High-rise buildings

    D   A lake

3. Where does Brian live in relation to the Yorkshire Dales?

    A   South

    B   North

    C   West

    D   East

4. Which of the following best describes Lucy's attitude to living in the countryside?

    A   She thinks moving to the countryside was a mistake.

    B   She has always loved living in the countryside.

    C   She was unsure at first, but she is beginning to enjoy it.

    D   She thinks that it is no match for city life.

5. Which of the following does Lucy enjoy most about living in the countryside?

    A   Going on walks

    B   Cosy nights in

    C   The fresh air

    D   The woolly lambs

6. Which of the following statements is false?

    A   Brian is fascinated by the countryside's scenery.

    B   Brian is looking forward to a weekend in the country.

    C   Brian finds life in the city tiring.

    D   Brian secretly wants to move to the countryside.

7. Lucy is described as a "reformed city slicker" (line 7). This means:

    A   she still prefers the fast-pace of city living.

    B   she does not understand rural ways of living.

    C   she has adjusted her urban way of life.

    D   she no longer visits cities.

8. Which of the following did Lucy enjoy before moving to the countryside?

    A   Living in a tourist hot-spot

    B   Eating high-quality food

    C   Travelling on the Underground

    D   Living in a tower block

TURN OVER ➡

9. Which of the following statements is false?

    A   Lucy's parents did not pack appropriately for their visit.

    B   Brian is unsure whether he's packed his trainers.

    C   Lucy told Brian to bring suitable clothing.

    D   Brian lives in the city.

10. Which of the following is not mentioned in the text?

    A   During which season Lucy moved to Yorkshire

    B   Who visited Lucy last week

    C   Where Brian has left his luggage

    D   Why Lucy moved to the countryside

11. What does "fascinated" (line 3) mean?

    A   Calmed

    B   Mesmerised

    C   Shocked

    D   Concerned

12. What does "vibrant" (line 16) mean?

    A   Radiant

    B   Dangerous

    C   Overwhelming

    D   Dynamic

END OF TEST

/ 12

Break time! These puzzles are a great way to test your **word knowledge** skills.

Word Snail

Use the clues below to fill in this word snail. The last letter of each word forms the first letter of the next word.

When you have completed the snail, unscramble the blue letters to reveal the hidden word.

1. To disagree strongly
2. No longer in existence
3. A person who betrays
4. To keep something
5. A person who cares for the sick and the injured
6. A person who sees something happen first-hand

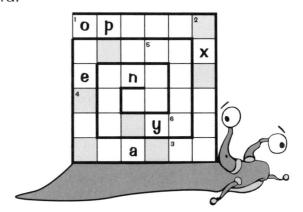

Hidden Word: A quiet and secluded place for relaxation: _____.

Cube Words

Using just the letters in the cube, can you find the answers to the clues? You can only use each letter once in each word.

H	C	L
L	E	G
N	A	E

Every answer must use the letter 'E'.

a large bird of prey ....

another word for 'peek' ....

a word relating to the law ....

a verb meaning 'alter' ....

Can you find the nine-letter word? _ _ _ _ _ _ _ _ _

Hint: it's another word for 'difficult'

45

You have **10 minutes** to do this test. Work as quickly and accurately as you can.

Read this passage carefully and answer the questions that follow.

The Listeners

'Is there anybody there?' said the Traveller,
　　Knocking on the moonlit door;
And his horse in the silence champed the grasses
　　Of the forest's ferny floor:
5　And a bird flew up out of the turret,
　　Above the Traveller's head:
And he smote* upon the door again a second time;
　　'Is there anybody there?' he said.
But no one descended to the Traveller;
10　　No head from the leaf-fringed sill
Leaned over and looked into his grey eyes,
　　Where he stood perplexed and still.
But only a host of phantom listeners
　　That dwelt in the lone house then
15　Stood listening in the quiet of the moonlight
　　To that voice from the world of men:
Stood thronging the faint moonbeams on the dark stair
　　That goes down to the empty hall,
Hearkening** in an air stirred and shaken
20　　By the lonely Traveller's call.
And he felt in his heart their strangeness,
　　Their stillness answering his cry,
While his horse moved, cropping the dark turf,
　　'Neath the starred and leafy sky;
25　For he suddenly smote on the door, even
　　Louder, and lifted his head:—
'Tell them I came, and no one answered,
　　That I kept my word,' he said.
Never the least stir made the listeners,
30　　Though every word he spake***
Fell echoing through the shadowiness of the still house
　　From the one man left awake:
Ay, they heard his foot upon the stirrup,
　　And the sound of iron on stone
35　And how the silence surged softly backward
　　When the plunging hoofs were gone.

Walter de la Mare

* smote — *hit*

** hearkening — *listening*

*** spake — *spoke*

Answer these questions about the text that you've just read.
Circle the letter that matches the correct answer.

1. When do the events of the poem take place?

   A   On a wet, stormy night

   B   On a still, clear night

   C   On the night of mid-winter

   D   On the night of a new moon

2. What information about the house is given in the poem?

   A   It's run down.

   B   It's very old.

   C   It's at the top of a hill.

   D   It's in a forest.

3. Which adjectives best describe the atmosphere at the house?

   A   Quiet and ghostly

   B   Sinister and threatening

   C   Chaotic and wild

   D   Peaceful and calm

4. What happens when the Traveller knocks on the door for the second time?

   A   A bird flies from one of the turrets of the house.

   B   Someone looks out of the window.

   C   Nothing happens.

   D   He sees two grey eyes staring at him.

TURN OVER ➡

5. Which word best describes how the Traveller feels in line 12?

    A   Anxious

    B   Confused

    C   Alone

    D   Impatient

6. What are the Traveller's thoughts in lines 21-22?

    A   He's irritated that he came all this way for nothing.

    B   He suspects that someone, or something, in the house can hear him.

    C   He thinks that the house is empty.

    D   He feels foolish for talking to thin air.

7. How do the listeners react to the Traveller?

    A   They ignore him because they can't hear him.

    B   They are angry that they have been disturbed.

    C   They feel sad because they can't respond to him.

    D   They stop and listen to him.

8. What is the horse doing when it is "cropping the dark turf" (line 23)?

    A   Stamping on the ground

    B   Eating the grass

    C   Eating the leaves off the trees

    D   Sniffing the undergrowth

9. Why does the Traveller go to the house?

   A   He needed to find shelter on his journey.

   B   He wanted to see the listeners for himself.

   C   He had made a promise to go there.

   D   He knew the people who used to live there.

10. Which of the following does not accurately describe the house?

   A   It has a turret.

   B   It has leaves growing around the windows.

   C   It has a broken chimney.

   D   It is silent.

11. "Never the least stir made the listeners" (line 29). What does this mean?

   A   The listeners choose to ignore the Traveller.

   B   The listeners move about to hear better.

   C   The listeners do not move.

   D   The listeners are heard by the Traveller.

12. What is making "the sound of iron on stone" (line 34)?

   A   The Traveller's boots on the ground

   B   The horse's hoofbeats on the ground

   C   The knocker banging on the door

   D   The door of the house finally creaking open

END OF TEST

/ 12

You have **10 minutes** to do this test. Work as quickly and accurately as you can.

Read this passage carefully and answer the questions that follow.

Timanfaya National Park

Between 1730 and 1736, violent volcanic eruptions hit the island of Lanzarote, creating an expansive lava field. Fifty square kilometres of the lava field is protected by the Timanfaya National Park in the western part of the island, and this area is referred to as Las Montañas del Fuego (the Fire Mountains).

5   The original eruptions were documented in the personal writings of a priest from the nearby village of Yaiza. Luckily, nobody was harmed by the volcanic debris, but the most fertile farmland on the island was destroyed, and villagers and farmers were forced to evacuate as entire villages were lost to the volcanoes.

The area is mostly desolate, made up of red, brown and grey rock with huge
10   craters. The landscape has remained fairly unchanged since the eruptions, as low rainfall has caused little erosion of the rock. Because of this, and the fact that the eruptions occurred relatively recently, the area is of particular interest to scientists and geographers who study changes in the land.

Despite its barren appearance, there is life in the area. You can find lizards, birds,
15   lichens and most recently, tourists. There is a lot to see in the park. A guided coach tour takes tourists around highlights of the volcanic wasteland, with a commentary describing the formation and history of the landscape. Visitors can also treat themselves to meat and fish grilled using the geothermal energy of the volcano, where temperatures a few meters below the surface reach 400-600°C. These intense
20   temperatures can be demonstrated by throwing water down a hole and watching it shoot back up in a jet of steam and hot water, and by placing hay into a pit and watching it start to burn without being lit. Despite this geothermal activity, the most recent eruption on the island took place in 1824, giving tourists and residents peace of mind.

Answer these questions about the text that you've just read.
Circle the letter that matches the correct answer.

1. Where are Las Montañas del Fuego located?

    A   In Timanfaya, a large lava field in Yaiza

    B   In Yaiza, a lava field near Timanfaya

    C   In Yaiza, a lava field in Lanzarote

    D   On the island of Lanzarote, near the village of Yaiza

2. Which of the following best describes why the area is called "Las Montañas del Fuego" (line 4)?

    A   The mountains were formed by lava from volcanic eruptions.

    B   The heat from the mountains can set a hay bale on fire.

    C   The mountains are shaped like flames.

    D   Locals wanted to use an exciting name to attract tourists.

3. According to the passage, what was an immediate consequence of the eruptions?

    A   The development of a thriving tourist industry.

    B   A large number of scientists are attracted to the area.

    C   A decrease in the amount of rainfall.

    D   The destruction of homes and livelihoods.

4. According to the passage, why has the landscape not changed much in 300 years?

    A   Volcanic rock is not easily affected by the weather.

    B   The dry climate has not caused much change or damage to the rock.

    C   Scientists have preserved the area.

    D   Geothermal heat keeps the land stable.

TURN OVER ➡

5. Which of the following statements is true?

   A   Hundreds of people were killed by the eruptions in the 18th century.

   B   The eruptions of 1730-6 were documented by a local farmer.

   C   Eruptions occurred in Lanzarote in the 18th and 19th centuries.

   D   The most recent eruption on Lanzarote occurred in the 18th century.

6. The last eruption in Lanzarote was almost 200 years ago.
   This gives tourists peace of mind because:

   A   they are hopeful it will erupt again soon.

   B   it is the most recent volcanic eruption.

   C   they believe the island is safe, as the volcano is unlikely to erupt.

   D   the eruption created an unusual lava field.

7. Timanfaya National Park is of interest to scientists because:

   A   there is plenty of interesting wildlife to study.

   B   changes to the landscape happened recently and are well preserved.

   C   temperatures close to the Earth's surface are unusually high.

   D   they want to predict when the next eruption will occur.

8. Which of the following is not mentioned in the passage?

   A   That lizards and birds have habitats in Timanfaya

   B   That there are demonstrations given of the volcanic heat

   C   That the landscape is made up of different-coloured rocks

   D   That there are small trees growing in the lava field

9. According to the passage, which of the following statements is true?

    A   Setting fire to hay creates intense heat on the surface.

    B   Visitors to Timanfaya National Park can watch volcanoes erupt.

    C   The underground heat can change water into steam.

    D   It is unsafe to eat meat which has been cooked geothermically.

10. Which of the following best explains "geothermal" (line 18)?

    A   Heat that is produced on the surface of the Earth

    B   Heat produced naturally inside the Earth

    C   An unusually strong heat

    D   Heat caused by an eruption

11. What does "expansive" (line 2) mean?

    A   Extensive

    B   Expanding

    C   Extraordinary

    D   Excessive

12. What does "commentary" (line 16) mean in the context of the passage?

    A   Critique

    B   Review

    C   Narration

    D   Annotation

END OF TEST

/ 12

(10)

You have **10 minutes** to do this test. Work as quickly and accurately as you can.

Read this passage carefully and answer the questions that follow.

An abridged extract from 'Little Women'

"'Mrs. Gardiner would be happy to see Miss March and Miss Josephine at a little dance on New Year's Eve.' Marmee* is willing we should go, now what shall we wear?"
"What's the use of asking that, when you know we shall wear our poplins**, because we haven't got anything else?" answered Jo with her mouth full.

5   "If I only had a silk!" sighed Meg. "Mother says I may when I'm eighteen perhaps, but two years is an everlasting time to wait."
"I'm sure our pops** look like silk, and they are nice enough for us. Yours is as good as new, but I forgot the burn and the tear in mine. Whatever shall I do? The burn shows badly, and I can't take any out."

10 "You must sit still all you can and keep your back out of sight. The front is all right. […] my gloves will do, though they aren't as nice as I'd like."
"Mine are spoiled with lemonade, and I can't get any new ones, so I shall have to go without," said Jo, who never troubled herself much about dress.
"You must have gloves, or I won't go," cried Meg decidedly. "Gloves are more

15 important than anything else. You can't dance without them, and if you don't I should be so mortified."
"Then I'll stay still. I don't care much for company dancing. It's no fun to go sailing round. I like to fly about and cut capers***."
"You can't ask Mother for new ones, they are so expensive, and you are so careless.

20 She said when you spoiled the others that she shouldn't get you any more this winter. Can't you make them do?"
"I can hold them crumpled up in my hand, so no one will know how stained they are. That's all I can do. No! I'll tell you how we can manage, each wear one good one and carry a bad one. Don't you see?"

* Marmee — *mother*

** poplins / pops — *cotton dresses*

*** cut capers — *leap playfully*

Louisa May Alcott

54

Answer these questions about the text that you've just read.
Circle the letter that matches the correct answer.

1. Why is Jo concerned about her dress?
   A   It doesn't fit.
   B   The back of it is damaged.
   C   The front of it is ripped.
   D   It has a lemonade stain on it.

2. How old is Jo?
   A   16
   B   17
   C   18
   D   It is not clear from the text.

3. Which of the following isn't suggested by Jo?
   A   That she won't wear gloves
   B   That she will borrow one of Meg's gloves
   C   That she will carry her gloves rather than wear them
   D   That she will buy a new pair of gloves

4. Why does Meg threaten not to attend the party?
   A   Because Jo might not wear gloves
   B   Because she doesn't have a silk dress
   C   Because she doesn't have any gloves
   D   Because she doesn't like dancing

TURN OVER ➡

5. Which of the following words best describes Jo?

   A   Sloppy

   B   Earnest

   C   Dreary

   D   Fussy

6. Which of the following statements is false?

   A   The girls' mother has given them permission to go to the party.

   B   Jo doesn't like formal dancing.

   C   Miss March has invited the girls to the party.

   D   Meg's dress is in good condition.

7. What is the most likely meaning of "can't take any out" (line 9)?

   A   Jo can't repair her dress by removing the damaged fabric.

   B   Jo doesn't have an alternative dress to wear.

   C   Jo can't alter the size of her dress.

   D   Jo can't wear her dress to the party.

8. Which of the following best describes Meg's attitude to the party?

   A   It is an occasion to meet people.

   B   It is a chance to dance with friends.

   C   It is an opportunity to dress up.

   D   It is an excellent way to celebrate the New Year.

9. What is the most likely meaning of "make them do" (line 21)?

   A   Clean them

   B   Manage with them

   C   Mend them

   D   Hide them from the other guests

10. Which of the following isn't given as a reason why Mother won't buy Jo new gloves?

   A   Gloves are costly.

   B   Jo often ruins her belongings.

   C   Jo has recently damaged a pair of gloves.

   D   Jo doesn't wear gloves often.

11. What does "decidedly" (line 14) mean?

   A   Decisively

   B   Bitterly

   C   Loudly

   D   Gloomily

12. What does "mortified" (line 16) mean?

   A   Upset

   B   Embarrassed

   C   Annoyed

   D   Resentful

END OF TEST

/ 12

Time for a break! This puzzle is a great way to sharpen up your **spelling** skills.

Spelling Treasures

The word grid on the right contains a hidden message that will lead you to some pirate loot.

Each of the seven sentences below has a number of spelling mistakes.

The number of mistakes in each sentence creates a co-ordinate. For example, if sentence A had 3 mistakes the co-ordinate would be (A,3).

Use these co-ordinates to reveal the hidden message and find the loot.

	A	B	C	D	E	F	G
5	A	coins	will be	stolen	near	your	statue
4	Some	opal	should be	hidden	on	a	pirates
3	An	gold	are	buried	by	some	shipwreck
2	The	diamond	is	located	under	the	cave
1	Your	treasure	have been	stashed	in	an	mountain

A. Geoff purchased eleven diffarent flavers of ice cream.

Co-ordinate: (A, ___)

B. Jennifer didn't like Nadya because she was constantly growning about something.

Co-ordinate: (B, ___)

C. Nick's granmother had recently turned ninty years old.

Co-ordinate: (C, ___)

D. Stuart was definately surprized to learn that lightening strikes the same place twice.

Co-ordinate: (D, ___)

E. Kara discuvered she had a fondness for caramel cookies.

Co-ordinate: (E, ___)

F. Jackson certainly gave a very convinceing performance.

Co-ordinate: (F, ___)

G. Abigail had been incredibly couragous when she confrunted the menacing bully.

Co-ordinate: (G, ___)

Hidden Message:

" _____ _____ _____ _____

_____ _____ _____ ."

⏱ 10

You have **10 minutes** to do this test. Work as quickly and accurately as you can.

Read this passage carefully and answer the questions that follow.

The Alchemist's Quest

There was once a wealthy duke who began to lose his sight. In despair, he ordered his servants to go into the nearest town to offer a vast reward to anyone who could restore his vision. Hearing these cries, a poor alchemist named Chang remembered a cure for blindness from an ancient text. According to the book, water
5 collected from the fabled lagoon of the western shores could make the blind see. Chang packed a few belongings and set off to discover the lagoon.

After several days, Chang reached a mysterious forest, but the lagoon proved hard to find. Tired and thirsty, he rested beside a river, and noticed a bird that had caught its wing in a trap. Gently, Chang untangled the bird from the snare; it flew a few
10 metres before turning to gaze at Chang.

Exhausted, Chang took shelter in an abandoned willow hut, where he decided to take another look at the ancient text. Alongside the description of the water's magical properties was a series of faint dashes positioned sporadically across the page, but Chang didn't understand what they meant. Eventually, he threw his hands
15 into the air and retired for the evening.

The next day, as Chang gathered his belongings, he noticed that a series of fork-shaped prints had appeared across the page. The dashes had been joined together by these prints, revealing a map of the forest and the legendary lagoon.

After following the map, Chang finally reached the lagoon. As he knelt by the
20 water's edge to fill a vial with water, he noticed the bird he had rescued sitting on a branch, its head cocked to one side. Chang rose to his feet, and bowed to the bird.

Upon his return, Chang successfully restored the wealthy man's sight with a few drops of liquid. Delighted, the duke showered Chang with gifts, making him one of the richest alchemists in the land.

TURN OVER ➡

Answer these questions about the text that you've just read.
Circle the letter that matches the correct answer.

1. Why did the duke send his servants into the town?

   A   To negotiate a reward for a remedy

   B   To find the person responsible for his deteriorating health

   C   To publicize a reward for a cure

   D   To announce that his health was deteriorating

2. What was the quest that Chang embarked on?

   A   The challenge of inventing a cure for blindness

   B   The discovery of an ancient text

   C   The act of freeing a trapped bird

   D   The journey to a faraway lagoon

3. According to the passage, which of the following statements is true?

   A   There was a sparrow caught in a trap.

   B   Chang rested by a river on the day he left for the forest.

   C   Fatigue and dehydration caused Chang to rest.

   D   Chang was the duke's servant.

4. Which of the following reasons is the most likely for Chang's journey?

   A   To be the first person to discover a cure for blindness

   B   To receive the reward

   C   To rescue the bird

   D   To test his own strength and courage

5. According to the passage, which of the following best describes Chang's text?

    A   It was an ancient novel about a lagoon.

    B   It was an old book, full of secrets.

    C   It was a book of natural remedies.

    D   It was a history book about the local area.

6. How did the bird help Chang?

    A   The bird used its footprints to make a map.

    B   The bird watched over Chang on his journey.

    C   Chang followed the bird to the lagoon.

    D   The bird filled the vial with water.

7. What is the most likely reason why the bird helped Chang?

    A   Because Chang was one of the wealthiest alchemists in the land

    B   To thank Chang for his help

    C   Because the bird admired Chang

    D   Because the bird wanted the duke to see again

8. Why did Chang throw "his hands into the air" (lines 14-15)?

    A   He is trying to catch the bird.

    B   He is frustrated by the book.

    C   He is stretching before he goes to sleep.

    D   He has worked out how to get to the lagoon.

TURN OVER ➡

9. Why does Chang bow to the bird?

    A   Because he is grateful for the bird's help

    B   Because he is relieved to have found the water

    C   Because he is exhausted and can't stand up straight

    D   Because he recognises the bird from earlier

10. Why did Chang become wealthy?

    A   He discovered a fabled lagoon.

    B   He distributed a cure for blindness.

    C   He was rewarded with expensive presents.

    D   He proved the validity of an ancient text.

11. What does "sporadically" (line 13) mean?

    A   Consistently

    B   Continuously

    C   Confusingly

    D   Intermittently

12. What does "vial" (line 20) mean?

    A   Bowl

    B   Jug

    C   Bottle

    D   Bucket

END OF TEST

/ 12

You have **10 minutes** to do this test. Work as quickly and accurately as you can.

> Read this passage carefully and answer the questions that follow.

The Boston Tea Party

Today, the thought of 342 crates of tea being destroyed would be enough to make most British people shiver. Yet in the December of 1773, this is exactly what happened in Boston, a city in the American state of Massachusetts. Boston locals were also partial to a cup of tea, so what drove them to empty more than 40 000 kg

5   of tea into the Boston harbour during what became known as The Boston Tea Party?

The Boston Tea Party was actually a protest against the British government. With the East India Company (EIC) struggling financially, the British government passed the Tea Act of 1773, which allowed the EIC to lower their tea prices. The EIC owed Britain money, so Britain hoped that allowing the EIC to undercut the competition

10   would prevent them from going bankrupt. Despite lower tea prices, the tea tax that Americans hoped would be removed remained in place, and Bostonians were unhappy about this interference in their trade.

When three shipments of tea arrived in Boston harbour, protestors argued that the tea should not be allowed on land, and should be sent back to England.

15   Some protestors took matters into their own hands. They disguised themselves as Mohawks*, boarded the ships and emptied the cargo into the harbour. Each ship's cargo was destroyed simultaneously, and it took the equivalent of one hour per ship to empty the tea. The loss of this tea would have cost around $1 000 000 or £650 000 today, so the British government responded by closing the ports in Boston

20   until the tea had been paid for.

The Boston Tea Party had many repercussions. Tea drinking amongst Americans declined as it was considered unpatriotic, and coffee became the new hot beverage of choice. More importantly, it caused further divides between Britain and the American people, which led to the American Revolution and eventually American

25   Independence some three years later.

* Mohawks — *a Native American tribe*   **TURN OVER** ➡

Answer these questions about the text that you've just read.
Circle the letter that matches the correct answer.

1. Where did the Boston Tea Party take place?

   A   In Boston, a state in America

   B   In Massachusetts, a city in Boston

   C   In Boston, a city in Britain

   D   In Massachusetts, a state in America

2. Which of the following best describes The Boston Tea Party?

   A   An anti-tea demonstration by Mohawk Indians

   B   An act of war in the American Revolution

   C   A revolt against decisions made by the British government

   D   An attack on British tradition

3. According to the passage, why did Britain allow changes to the price of tea?

   A   Britain wanted to make tea more profitable.

   B   Britain needed more money to repay the EIC.

   C   Britain wanted to punish the people of Boston for disobedience.

   D   Britain wanted to keep the EIC out of debt, so the EIC could afford to repay
          its debts to Britain.

4. According to the passage, what is the main reason that the Boston locals opposed
   the Tea Act?

   A   They opposed the British government interfering with their trade.

   B   They wanted cheaper tea to drink.

   C   They wanted to start a revolution that would lead to independence.

   D   They could no longer afford the price of tea.

5. According to the text, which of the following reasons best explains why some protestors dressed as Mohawks?

    A   To gain access to the ships more easily

    B   To remain anonymous

    C   To make a political statement

    D   To draw attention to the protest

6. Which of the following best describes why the tea was thrown into the harbour?

    A   In order to bankrupt the EIC

    B   In order to blame the issue on the Mohawk people

    C   As an act of defiance

    D   In order to show solidarity with the EIC

7. Which of the following statements is false?

    A   All three shipments of tea were destroyed at the same time.

    B   Boston is situated on the coast.

    C   The EIC had borrowed money from the British government.

    D   Britain closed Boston's ports for three years.

8. Which of the following statements is true?

    A   After 1773, coffee became the most popular drink amongst Americans.

    B   Before 1773, tea was more popular than coffee amongst Americans.

    C   After 1773, drinking coffee was considered patriotic by Americans.

    D   Before 1773, drinking coffee was unpopular amongst Americans.

TURN OVER ➡

9. According to the passage, which of the following statements is false?

    A   The protestors destroyed 342 crates of tea.

    B   The protestors destroyed over 40 000 kg of tea.

    C   The protestors destroyed three shipments of tea.

    D   The protestors destroyed £1 000 000 of tea.

10. According to the passage, how did the British government respond to the protest?

    A   They prevented ships from sailing into Boston harbour.

    B   They increased taxes on tea in Boston.

    C   They declared the start of the American Revolution.

    D   They stopped importing tea to Boston.

11. Which of the following is not mentioned in the passage?

    A   The year that the Boston Tea Party took place.

    B   The month that the Boston Tea Party took place.

    C   The value of the tea when it was thrown into the harbour.

    D   The number of crates of tea that were emptied into the harbour.

12. According to the text, when did America declare their independence?

    A   The 17th century

    B   The 18th century

    C   The 19th century

    D   The 20th century

END OF TEST

/ 12

You have **10 minutes** to do this test. Work as quickly and accurately as you can.

Read this passage carefully and answer the questions that follow.

'The Village Blacksmith' by Henry W. Longfellow

Under a spreading chestnut-tree
    The village smithy stands;
The smith, a mighty man is he,
    With large and sinewy hands;
5   And the muscles of his brawny arms
    Are strong as iron bands.

His hair is crisp, and black, and long;
    His face is like the tan;
His brow is wet with honest sweat,
10   He earns whate'er he can,
And looks the whole world in the face,
    For he owes not any man.

Week in, week out, from morn till night,
    You can hear his bellows blow;
15 You can hear him swing his heavy sledge,
    With measured beat and slow,
Like a sexton* ringing the village bell,
    When the evening sun is low.

And children coming home from school
20   Look in at the open door;
They love to see the flaming forge,
    And hear the bellows roar,
And catch the burning sparks that fly
    Like chaff from a threshing-floor**

25 He goes on Sunday to the church,
    And sits among his boys;
He hears the parson pray and preach,
    He hears his daughter's voice
Singing in the village choir,
30   And it makes his heart rejoice.

It sounds to him like her mother's voice,
    Singing in Paradise!
He needs must think of her once more,
    How in the grave she lies;
35 And with his hard, rough hand he wipes
    A tear out of his eyes.

Toiling,—rejoicing,—sorrowing,
    Onward through life he goes;
Each morning sees some task begin,
40   Each evening sees it close;
Something attempted, something done,
    Has earned a night's repose.

Thanks, thanks to thee, my worthy friend,
    For the lesson thou hast taught!
45 Thus at the flaming forge of life
    Our fortunes must be wrought;
Thus on its sounding anvil shaped
    Each burning deed and thought.

* sexton — *a church official*
** chaff/threshing-floor — *husks of corn / the surface on which the corn is separated from its husks*

TURN OVER

Answer these questions about the text that you've just read.
Circle the letter that matches the correct answer.

1. Where is the blacksmith's workshop located?

    A   Next to a chestnut tree

    B   Near a school

    C   In a tiny hamlet

    D   On the outskirts of a town

2. The blacksmith's brow is "wet with honest sweat" (line 9). This means:

    A   that he stands next to the flames all day.

    B   that he works hard to earn a living.

    C   that he charges a fair price for his work.

    D   that he is a reliable individual.

3. Which of the following statements must be false?

    A   The blacksmith works to pay off his debts.

    B   The blacksmith works long hours.

    C   The blacksmith takes some time off on Sundays.

    D   The blacksmith accepts all the work he is offered.

4. Why is the blacksmith compared to a church official in line 17?

    A   Because he is a religious man

    B   Because he is an honest man

    C   Because his work has a music-like rhythm to it

    D   Because he works late into the evening

5. Which of the following would not be used to describe the blacksmith?

    A   He is pale.

    B   He has long hair.

    C   He is a widower.

    D   He has dark hair.

6. The blacksmith is described as looking "the whole world in the face" (line 11).
    This means that:

    A   he always keeps eye contact with his customers.

    B   he believes he is a decent man.

    C   he isn't afraid to confront people who disagree with him.

    D   he isn't intimidated by hard work.

7. Which of the following statements is false?

    A   The schoolchildren love listening to the noises of the smithy.

    B   The schoolchildren love catching the sparks that fly around the smithy.

    C   The schoolchildren love catching the corn husks that fly around the smithy.

    D   The schoolchildren love watching the fire in the smithy.

8. Which of the following statements is true?

    A   His daughter's voice reminds him of his mother.

    B   His daughter's voice reminds him of his wife.

    C   His daughter's voice makes his heart beat faster.

    D   His daughter's voice reminds him of an angel.

TURN OVER ➡

9. Which of the following causes the blacksmith to become emotional?

    A   Thinking about his mother

    B   Thinking about his wife

    C   Hearing his daughter sing

    D   Hearing the parson preach

10. The blacksmith is described as "Toiling, —rejoicing, —sorrowing" (line 37). Which of the following causes the blacksmith to rejoice?

    A   Accomplishing an honest day's work

    B   Raising a family

    C   Hearing his daughter sing in the village choir

    D   Entertaining the schoolchildren as they walk past

11. What does "sledge" (line 15) mean?

    A   Shovel

    B   Hammer

    C   Poker

    D   Axe

12. What does "Toiling" (line 37) mean?

    A   Worrying

    B   Struggling

    C   Battling

    D   Working

END OF TEST

/ 12

Time for a break! These teasers are a great way to sharpen up your **logic** skills.

Scene of the Crime

Detective Dudley has a new case, but he needs some help finding the criminal.

Use his notes below to work out who committed the crime, and explain how you came to this conclusion.

- Mrs. Walker's watch was stolen on a rainy Sunday morning at 10:30 am.
- Mrs. Walker was asleep at the time of the incident.
- Mr. Walker was cooking a family breakfast.
- Their son Jackson was tidying his bedroom.
- Mr. Potts was watering his garden.
- Mrs. Crumb the baker was kneading some dough.
- Miss Steel the mechanic was changing a tyre.
- One of the people above is definitely lying.

Who committed the crime? _____

How did you come to this conclusion?

_____

Riddle Me Timbers

There are six pieces of treasure in a chest. Six pirates decide to split the treasure evenly between them, so they each get one piece.

Therefore, how can one of the pieces still be in the chest?

_____

_____

(10)

You have **10 minutes** to do this test. Work as quickly and accurately as you can.

Read this passage carefully and answer the questions that follow.

Edith Smith's Memoirs

Next week I turn 100 years old; that will be 36 525 days on planet Earth. I've seen the months fly by, the seasons change and some leap years. Each of those days made me who I am today, and hopefully these memoirs will be preserved for future generations of the Smith family to enjoy.

5   I was born on October 23rd 1915, the decade the First World War began, and I was married 19 years later on 2nd November, during the decade that the Second World War began. Although that might seem like a bad omen to many, I have had an extremely happy life and marriage. I embarked upon a career as a receptionist in 1936, but I gave it up when my children came along in the 1940s. I've never lost

10   my ability to use a typewriter though, and I use an electronic typewriter for all my correspondence.

One of the greatest blessings of reaching this age is how much I have seen my family develop. I am lucky enough to have known several generations before me, and now I am able to appreciate not only my three children, but my five

15   grandchildren and two great-grandchildren.

I especially love it when my children come over to visit. My husband and I bake a cake without fail, and for each of their birthdays we make their favourite. For Matthew's 72nd birthday last month we baked him a black forest gateau, and Sue always has a Victoria sponge for her birthday in December. However, my eyesight

20   isn't what it was, so I won't be able to keep it up much longer.

I have lived a rich life full of experience, something I dearly hope you all get to do. Never doubt, and never worry; the only thing worse than failure is a failure to try. I read that in an old book, but it is something I have lived by since. I have to change my reading habits now, but the library has CDs I can listen to. They're not as

25   good, but they do the job.

Answer these questions about the text that you've just read.
Circle the letter that matches the correct answer.

1. If there are 365 days in a year, why has Edith lived for nearly 36 525 days?

   A   Edith has included an extra year by mistake.

   B   There are not 365 days every year.

   C   Edith was not counting leap years.

   D   Edith is not as good at maths as she once was.

2. What reason does Edith give for writing her memoirs?

   A   She wants her family to live life to the fullest.

   B   She wants to write things down while she can still see.

   C   She wants her family to be able to read about her life.

   D   She wants to explain every day she has enjoyed.

3. According to the text, when did the Second World War begin?

   A   1910s

   B   1920s

   C   1930s

   D   1940s

4. Which of the following statements is true?

   A   Edith became a receptionist during the First World War.

   B   Edith was 19 years old when she became a receptionist.

   C   Edith was married when she became a receptionist.

   D   Edith was a mother when she became a receptionist.

TURN OVER ➡

5. According to the passage, how long did Edith's career as a receptionist last?

    A   Four years

    B   Less than five years

    C   Over eight years

    D   It is unclear from the text

6. According to her memoirs, which of the following does Edith think makes up the person she is today?

    A   The experience she has had every day of her life

    B   Every member of her family

    C   The things she has read in various books

    D   Her age

7. Which of the following is contained in the passage?

    A   The name of Edith's eldest child

    B   How many years Edith has been married

    C   How many years she has been writing her memoirs

    D   Edith's husband's name

8. Which of the following statements must be true?

    1. Edith's children have 5 children between them.

    2. Edith has 10 other people in her family.

    3. Edith's children all have the same number of children.

    4. Some of Edith's children now have grandchildren.

    A   1 and 2

    B   2 and 3

    C   2 and 4

    D   1 and 4

9. Which of the following statements is false?

   A   Edith writes letters on her typewriter.

   B   Sue's favourite cake is Victoria sponge.

   C   Edith is 100 years old at the time of writing.

   D   Edith listens to audio versions of books.

10. Which of the following statements must be true?

   A   Matthew's birthday is in September

   B   Sue is older than Matthew

   C   Matthew was born in 1948

   D   Sue was born on 23rd October

11. Which of the following statements is true?

   A   Edith thinks doubt and worry lead to failure.

   B   Edith enjoys failure because it proves she has tried.

   C   Edith thinks that failure is something to be afraid of.

   D   Edith thinks that not attempting something is worse than failure.

12. Edith's biggest wish for her family is:

   A   that they don't forget her.

   B   that they live a full and enriching life.

   C   that they live to be as old as she is.

   D   that they get to experience life exactly as she has.

END OF TEST

/ 12

You have **10 minutes** to do this test. Work as quickly and accurately as you can.

Read this passage carefully and answer the questions that follow.

Arthur Conan Doyle

Sherlock Holmes is arguably the world's most famous fictional detective, often portrayed with a distinctive deerstalker hat on his head and a magnifying glass in his hand. But the inspiration behind the perceptive Victorian sleuth is less well-known. Arthur Conan Doyle, Holmes's creator, reportedly based his character on a surgeon
5   named Joseph Bell. Bell taught Doyle at university, and used a similar process of deduction to diagnose illnesses as Sherlock used to solve mysteries.

Although Sherlock Holmes is now a household name, Doyle initially found it hard to find a publisher. He received several rejection letters, and when he finally sold the copyright for his book, it attracted little attention. Undeterred, he continued
10 his Holmes series, and eventually the detective became a much-loved figure.

Ultimately, the Sherlock Holmes mysteries began to commandeer much of Doyle's time, and prevented him from pursuing other projects. In response to this, Doyle increased the fees for his Holmes stories in an attempt to curb his publisher's appetite. Instead, they simply paid him more than he requested. In 1893, Doyle
15 killed Holmes off to avoid writing any more stories.

Doyle lived an exciting and varied life. His adventures included being a surgeon on a whaling ship, leading him to write the short story 'Captain of the Pole Star'; he ran for Parliament twice but was unsuccessful; he volunteered for the Boer War but was too overweight to be declared fit, so instead volunteered as a medical doctor.
20 He was also a keen amateur footballer and cricketer.

In 1902, King Edward VII knighted Doyle for his part in the Boer War, but since the monarch was supposedly a keen reader of the Holmes series, the knighthood might have been used to encourage Doyle to pick up his pen once more. In 1903, Doyle revived the great detective due to public demand.

Answer these questions about the text that you've just read.
Circle the letter that matches the correct answer.

1. What do Sherlock Holmes and Joseph Bell have in common?

   A   They are both surgeons.

   B   They are the same person.

   C   They are both good at solving problems.

   D   They both use magnifying glasses.

2. What was Doyle's early experience in the publishing world?

   A   He struggled to get his story published.

   B   He sold the copyright quickly.

   C   He sold his first book for a large amount of money.

   D   He became a household name.

3. According to the text, the Holmes stories:

   A   were based on Doyle's ability to diagnose patients.

   B   were less popular than Doyle's other works.

   C   brought Doyle instant success.

   D   did not stop Doyle from having an adventurous life.

4. Which of the following is the most likely reason why Holmes became such a well-known character?

   A   His popularity with readers

   B   His deerstalker hat was very recognisable

   C   Doyle's connection to Joseph Bell

   D   Doyle's adventurous lifestyle

TURN OVER ➡

5. According to the passage, which of the following is true?

    A   Doyle studied medicine at university.

    B   Doyle fought in the Boer War.

    C   Doyle was the captain of a whaling ship.

    D   Doyle was a Member of Parliament.

6. Which of the following best describes Sherlock Holmes?

    A   Cunning

    B   Obnoxious

    C   Infamous

    D   Insightful

7. Why did Doyle begin to charge more money for his stories?

    A   Because he needed more money

    B   So his publishers would stop demanding more stories

    C   Because he felt his stories were worth more money

    D   Because his publishers were making him work longer hours

8. Why do you think Doyle might have resented the success of his Sherlock Holmes stories?

    A   Holmes's popularity meant he didn't have time to pursue other things.

    B   Doyle thought his other stories were better.

    C   He sold the copyright early, so he didn't benefit from their success.

    D   Writing about Holmes meant Doyle had to give up a career in politics.

9. How did Doyle attempt to end his Sherlock Holmes series?

    A   Holmes finished a difficult case.

    B   Holmes retired.

    C   Holmes was replaced by another character.

    D   Holmes died.

10. Why did Doyle bring back Holmes?

    A   King Edward VII demanded it

    B   Doyle's other stories were a flop

    C   He ran out of money

    D   His fans urged him to

11. What does "portrayed" (line 2) mean?

    A   Depicted

    B   Disguised

    C   Remembered

    D   Connected

12. What does "supposedly" (line 22) mean?

    A   Allegedly

    B   Definitely

    C   Hesitantly

    D   Obviously

END OF TEST

/ 12

You have **10 minutes** to do this test. Work as quickly and accurately as you can.

> Read this passage carefully and answer the questions that follow.

An extract from 'The Yellow Wallpaper'

    John is practical in the extreme. He has no patience with faith, an intense horror of superstition, and he scoffs openly at any talk of things not to be felt and seen and put down in figures.

    John is a physician*, and PERHAPS — (I would not say it to a living soul, of
5   course, but this is dead paper and a great relief to my mind) — PERHAPS that is one reason I do not get well faster.

    You see he does not believe I am sick!

    And what can one do?

    If a physician of high standing, and one's own husband, assures friends and
10 relatives that there is really nothing the matter with one but temporary nervous depression — a slight hysterical tendency** — what is one to do?

    My brother is also a physician, and also of high standing, and he says the same thing.

    So I take phosphates or phosphites — whichever it is, and tonics, and journeys,
15 and air, and exercise, and am absolutely forbidden to "work" until I am well again.

    Personally, I disagree with their ideas.

    Personally, I believe that congenial*** work, with excitement and change, would do me good.

    But what is one to do?

20   I did write for a while in spite of them; but it DOES exhaust me a good deal — having to be so sly about it, or else meet with heavy opposition.

    I sometimes fancy that in my condition if I had less opposition and more society and stimulus — but John says the very worst thing I can do is to think about my condition, and I confess it always makes me feel bad.

                               Charlotte Perkins Gilman

* physician — *doctor*

** hysterical tendency — *a tendency to get very upset or agitated*

*** congenial — *enjoyable*

1. Which of the following best describes John?

    A   He is sympathetic.

    B   He is unpleasant.

    C   He is distrustful.

    D   He is a realist.

2. Which of the following best explains why John does not think his wife is ill?

    A   She does not show many signs of pain.

    B   He does not like to think of her being unwell.

    C   Her illness is not a physical one.

    D   He believes his wife has a vivid imagination.

3. Which of the following does the narrator believe might be slowing her recovery?

    A   That she has to exercise

    B   That she is married to a doctor

    C   That she has to take tonics

    D   That John has no patience with faith

4. Which of the following statements is not true?

    A   John does not believe his wife is sick.

    B   The narrator's brother is a doctor.

    C   The narrator has to take phosphates and phosphites.

    D   John does not believe in superstition.

TURN OVER ➡

5. Which of the following statements is not mentioned in the passage?

   A   The narrator believes excitement would improve her condition.

   B   The narrator believes work would improve her condition.

   C   The narrator believes the company of others would improve her condition.

   D   The narrator believes that time will improve her condition.

6. Which of the following is not part of the narrator's treatment?

   A   Getting out of the house for walks

   B   Thinking about her illness

   C   Taking regular journeys

   D   Getting fresh air

7. Which of the following best describes why the narrator likes to write?

   A   It allows her to say things she couldn't normally say to anyone else.

   B   It takes her mind off her illness.

   C   She likes to write about congenial things.

   D   She wants her husband and brother to read what she has written.

8. What does the narrator find exhausting about writing?

   A   Coming up with ideas

   B   Holding a pen for too long

   C   Keeping it a secret

   D   When people disagree with what she writes

9. Which of the following words best describes how the narrator feels in lines 7-11?

    A   Frustrated

    B   Impatient

    C   Miserable

    D   Tolerant

10. What does "scoffs" (line 2) mean?

    A   Discusses

    B   Complains

    C   Mocks

    D   Frets

11. What does "high standing" (line 9) mean?

    A   Imposing

    B   Well-regarded

    C   Highly educated

    D   Very experienced

12. What is the most likely meaning of "dead paper" (line 5)?

    A   That the paper will get destroyed

    B   That the paper is lifeless, so won't tell anyone what she has written

    C   That she is actually not writing anything down

    D   That she is writing on old pieces of paper

END OF TEST

/ 12

Time for a break! This puzzle is a great way to practise your **word-making** skills.

Compound Clues

Each of the nine boxes below contains a clue.

Use these clues to write down nine words or phrases. An example is shown to the right.

Half of each answer is written in the clue — the other half is the way the clue is presented.

D
N
U
O
R

..........**round-up**..........

 FISH

....

EHCA

....

 WORM

....

NDSANDSAND

....

MOON

....

KEY

....

CODE

....

 BROTHER

....

TIMETIMETIMETIME

....

You have **10 minutes** to do this test. Work as quickly and accurately as you can.

Read this passage carefully and answer the questions that follow.

Rainy Day at the Zoo

Threatening black clouds had been scuttling across the sky all day, so when Ellis and Thea were met with persistent drizzle at the gates of the zoo, they weren't surprised. However, after a rousing pep talk from Ellis, Thea decided that a spot of bad luck shouldn't dampen their spirits, and their outing should go ahead as
5   planned.
The first area they visited contained a herd of meerkats. Eagerly, Ellis took out his camera to take a few shots. The click of the shutter caused the meerkats to turn and face him, ears pricked and whiskers twitching. When the next click sounded, the group scurried in myriad directions, fleeing into their burrows. The duo soon
10 grew bored of looking at an empty, muddy enclosure, and ventured off in search of something more interesting.
As they headed towards the elephant enclosure, the rain started to fall even harder. Drizzle turned into showers, which turned into pelting rain, and the plan to head to the outdoor elephant enclosure was soon abandoned in favour
15 of the lynx exhibit. Exposed to the rain, Thea's map of the zoo had turned into incomprehensible mush; using a signpost, she suggested that the indoor exhibit was only a short walk away, and would offer a brief respite from the elements. Unfortunately, when they arrived, everyone else seemed to have had the same idea, and the queue for the lynx exhibition spilled out of the door.
20 At this point, even Ellis's spirits were beginning to flag. Their high expectations had been met with a few soggy meerkats and some bare, sodden paddocks. Even the seagulls that usually loitered near the picnic area had vanished. Neither Thea nor Ellis wanted to admit that their trip had been a wash-out, but when Thea suggested that she might catch an earlier bus home, Ellis was very keen to join her.

TURN OVER ➡

Answer these questions about the text that you've just read.
Circle the letter that matches the correct answer.

1. Thea and Ellis decide that the weather won't "dampen their spirits" (line 4).
    This means:

    A   Thea and Ellis plan to stay dry.

    B   they are perfectly happy in the rain.

    C   they are determined to have a good time.

    D   they are disheartened by the weather.

2. Which of the following best describes the meerkats' reaction to the camera?

    A   Alert then frightened

    B   Relaxed then curious

    C   Alert then curious

    D   Frightened then relaxed

3. The meerkats are described as scurrying in "myriad directions" (line 9).
    This means:

    A   the meerkats ran away in pairs

    B   the meerkats ran away in the same direction.

    C   the meerkats ran away in lots of different directions.

    D   the meerkats ran away in two opposite directions.

4. Which of the following best describes why Ellis and Thea are looking at an
    empty enclosure?

    A   They are waiting for the meerkats to reappear.

    B   They are sheltering from the rain.

    C   They want to catch sight of a meerkat.

    D   They are deciding which enclosure to visit next.

5. According to the text, why do Ellis and Thea decide not to visit the elephant enclosure?

    A   They decide they would rather see the lynx.

    B   They are disheartened after scaring the meerkats.

    C   The elephant enclosure is closed.

    D   The weather gets worse.

6. Which of the following best describes Thea's map?

    A   It is clear and easy to understand.

    B   It is unhelpful and hard to read.

    C   It is soggy and impossible to read.

    D   It is poorly designed and hard to use.

7. Why do Thea and Ellis decide to visit the lynx enclosure?

    A   It is nearby.

    B   It is the zoo's star attraction.

    C   It is indoors.

    D   The elephant enclosure is shut.

8. Which of the following statements must be false?

    A   Ellis is a keen photographer.

    B   The rain catches Thea and Ellis off guard.

    C   Meerkats are easily spooked.

    D   The elephant enclosure is unpopular.

TURN OVER ➡

9. Which of the following statements is true?

   A   The only animals they see are seagulls.

   B   Thea keeps Ellis's spirits high.

   C   Ellis wants to leave the zoo early.

   D   The duo did not expect a lot from the zoo.

10. Thea and Ellis are reluctant to "admit that their trip had been a wash-out" (line 23). This means:

   A   they don't want to admit that their trip has been ruined by the rain.

   B   they don't want to admit that they have found the zoo boring.

   C   they don't want to admit that they are disappointed by the zoo.

   D   they don't want to admit that they want to leave the zoo early.

11. What does "persistent" (line 2) mean?

   A   Continual

   B   Interrupted

   C   Light

   D   Heavy

12. What does "rousing" (line 3) mean?

   A   Intense

   B   Inspiring

   C   Despondent

   D   Insincere

END OF TEST

/ 12

Test 21

You have **10 minutes** to do this test. Work as quickly and accurately as you can.

Read this passage carefully and answer the questions that follow.

The Children's War

Between 3rd September 1939 and 2nd September 1945, Britain fought in World War Two against Germany. During this time, many British cities, especially London, were bombed. German planes aimed to destroy factories, ports and industrial centres. The civilian population needed to brace itself against these attacks.

5 Even before war was declared, the government was worried about how to cope with potential enemy attacks, and it was soon decided that British cities were unsafe. On 1st September 1939, a mass exodus of children from the cities to the countryside began. By the end of the war, around 3.5 million people, mainly children, had been evacuated.

10 Most evacuees were given a name tag and travelled by train with a small bag of clean clothes, washing things and a few toys from home. Once in the countryside, children were assembled in village halls and taken in by 'host families' — people from the local community.

Lots of children enjoyed life as an evacuee, relishing the opportunity to see the
15 countryside — many had never seen cows or chickens before. They had caring hosts, made friends at school, and wrote letters home to keep in touch. For other children, evacuation was an ordeal. They missed their parents, didn't make new friends easily and found their new surroundings confusing.

By January 1940, there had still been no bombing in Britain. People called this
20 the 'Phoney War', and around 50% of evacuees returned to the cities. However, many went back to the countryside when bombing began later in the year.

Not all city children were evacuated — some parents wanted their families to stick together, and children continued to live at home. If there was an attack, they used air-raid shelters in gardens and public places for protection. In London, many
25 families sheltered in underground stations, often taking bedding and board games and spending the whole night there.

TURN OVER ➡

Answer these questions about the text that you've just read.
Circle the letter that matches the correct answer.

1. According to the passage, what did the civilian population have to prepare for?

    A   Defending their country from attacks

    B   A war on foreign soil

    C   Attacks on British cities

    D   Moving to the countryside

2. When did the government start to evacuate children?

    A   Before war was declared

    B   The day war was declared

    C   After war was declared

    D   During the Phoney War

3. The author states there was a "mass exodus of children from the cities" (line 7). What does this mean?

    A   Lots of children lived close to the cities.

    B   Lots of children were excited about evacuation.

    C   Lots of city children ran away from home.

    D   Lots of children moved out of the cities.

4. Which of the following is not mentioned in the passage?

    A   Factories and ports were targets.

    B   Parents gave their children name tags.

    C   Some evacuees wrote letters home to their parents.

    D   Evacuees lived with families in village communities.

5. According to the passage, which of these statements is false?

    A   Most evacuees found evacuation to be an ordeal.

    B   Most evacuees travelled by train.

    C   Most evacuees took a small bag of belongings with them.

    D   Most evacuees were given a name tag.

6. According to the passage, what was the "Phoney War" (line 20)?

    A   The years when the threat of war was not real.

    B   A time when nothing was bombed in Europe.

    C   A period when there was no bombing in Britain.

    D   The January of 1940, when bombing had not yet begun.

7. According to the passage, why were some city children not evacuated?

    A   Because there were air-raid shelters available

    B   Because their parents didn't want them to go

    C   Because they missed their parents

    D   Because the cities were safe

8. How do you think the author would most likely summarise evacuation?

    A   It wasn't necessary because of the Phoney War.

    B   It was a fantastic opportunity to see the countryside.

    C   It was a frightening and confusing ordeal for children.

    D   It was a difficult but necessary process.

TURN OVER ➡

9. According to the passage, where might city children have taken shelter from bombing?

    A   Factories

    B   Underground stations

    C   Garden sheds

    D   Neighbours' houses

10. By the end of the war, how many evacuees had been sent to the countryside?

    A   2.1 million people

    B   50% of children

    C   Around 3.5 million

    D   50% of the population

11. What does the word "relishing" (line 14) mean?

    A   Tolerating

    B   Acknowledging

    C   Savouring

    D   Resenting

12. What does the word "ordeal" (line 17) mean?

    A   Pleasure

    B   Trial

    C   Nuisance

    D   Experience

END OF TEST

/ 12

You have **10 minutes** to do this test. Work as quickly and accurately as you can.

Read this passage carefully and answer the questions that follow.

Jane and the Plane

"Boarding pass, please," said the flight attendant. With a shaking hand, Jane grappled with her tatty holdall, and handed over the thin piece of paper she had kept a tight grip on all day. "Thank you very much, and enjoy your flight to Madrid."

Jane had always been wary of people who smiled too much: she thought it 5 appeared insincere. Flying was certainly not an act to be enjoyed, but rather one to be tolerated for the greater good of the family holiday.

The children didn't agree; they were both extremely excited, especially Michael, pulling his wheeled suitcase behind him with pride. It was such an adventure! He had never met his foreign relatives before, and this was his first holiday abroad after 10 years of trips and vacations around the UK.

"You'll be fine," David told her, picking up his pristine leather suitcase. "Just try to relax. It's only a short flight, and then we'll have two weeks in the sun." Jane gave a slight smile, but the muscles in her face were too tense for it to appear natural. As they boarded the plane, she started to look for their seats.

15 "21C… 22C…" she muttered under her breath, "23C! Here we are, kids; in you get." Michael and Lucy giddily bounced into their seats, and despite her nerves, Jane relaxed for just a moment.

She looked back at David in row 26, putting Lucy's pink backpack in the luggage hold. He gave her a warm smile, and she was finally able to give him a genuine 20 smile. She sat down in her seat and gave her children a kiss on the forehead.

"Eurgh, Mum!" Michael exclaimed, "What did you do that for?" Jane laughed for the first time all day; she knew that as long as her children were with her, everything would be fine.

TURN OVER ➡

93

1. Why is Jane described as having "a tight grip" on her boarding pass (line 3)?

    A   Because it is needed to get on the plane

    B   Because she wants to keep it as a souvenir

    C   Because she has to hand it over to the attendant

    D   Because she does not want to fly

2. Which of the following best describes why Jane is on the plane?

    A   So that she can have a relaxing holiday

    B   So that Michael can have an adventure

    C   So that the family can have a holiday together

    D   So that she can face her fear of flying

3. According to the text, which of the following is true?

    A   Jane's smile always looks unnatural.

    B   Jane is irritated by people who smile.

    C   Jane only smiles at her children.

    D   Jane does not always find smiles comforting.

4. Which of the following best describes Jane's thoughts about flying?

    A   It is something that must be endured.

    B   It is something the whole family can enjoy.

    C   It is unnecessary and could be avoided.

    D   It is something children love to do.

5. Why does Jane mutter the seat numbers "under her breath" (line 15)?

   A   She is nervous about finding her seat.

   B   She does not want her children to hear.

   C   She is thinking out loud.

   D   She doesn't want to make a fuss in front of the other passengers.

6. Which of the following statements must be false?

   A   Jane's holdall is a bit shabby.

   B   David's canvas suitcase is spotless.

   C   Michael's suitcase has wheels.

   D   Lucy's luggage has straps.

7. According to the passage, which of the following statements must be false?

   A   They have family in another country.

   B   Michael has never been on holiday before.

   C   The family are not sitting together on the plane.

   D   This is Michael's first time on a plane.

8. Which of the following is not mentioned in the passage?

   A   Where the family are flying to

   B   Who the family are going to visit

   C   How long the family are going away for

   D   How long the flight will last

TURN OVER ➡

9. What first causes Jane to relax before the flight?

    A   David's reassuring words

    B   Having her children nearby

    C   Her children's enthusiasm

    D   David's smile

10. Which of the following best describes how Jane feels at the end of the passage?

    A   At ease

    B   Uncertain

    C   Excited

    D   Concerned

11. What does "wary" (line 4) mean?

    A   Suspicious

    B   Fearful

    C   Petrified

    D   Nervous

12. What does "tense" (line 13) mean?

    A   Shaky

    B   Tight

    C   Swollen

    D   Brittle

END OF TEST

/ 12

These puzzles are a great way to sharpen your **word-making** and **sentence** skills. Hooray!

Cryptogram Conundrum

You only need to work out the numbers that correspond to the letters in the message.

The message below has been written in code.

Start with the shortest word. Using the letters provided, work out what the most likely missing letter could be. Once you think you've worked it out, check to see whether you can add that letter anywhere else. Then add it to the grid, and move on to another number.

You'll have to use your knowledge of word formation along with a bit of trial and error to solve the puzzle!

```
__  H  __  __  __  __  __  __      H  __  __  __  __  __      —
14   8   4  10  15   3  23  19      8   3  15  13   4  14

T   H  __     __  __  __  A   T     __  __  T  __  T  __  __  __
26   8   4     20  10   4  21  26    11   4  26   4  23  26  18   1   4
```

A	B	C	D	E	F	G	H	I	J	K	L	M	N	O	P	Q	R	S	T	U	V	W	X	Y	Z
21							8												26						

Word Square

How many words can you make from the letters in this word square?

Each letter must only be used once per word and each word must be at least three letters long.

Hidden in the grid is a nine-letter word.

C	E	T
U	L	C
A	L	A

....

....

....

....

You have **10 minutes** to do this test. Work as quickly and accurately as you can.

Read this passage carefully and answer the questions that follow.

An extract from 'London Snow'

When men were all asleep the snow came flying,
In large white flakes falling on the city brown,
Stealthily and perpetually settling and loosely lying,
    Hushing the latest traffic of the drowsy town;
5 Deadening, muffling, stifling its murmurs failing;
Lazily and incessantly floating down and down:
    Silently sifting and veiling road, roof and railing;
Hiding difference, making unevenness even,
Into angles and crevices softly drifting and sailing.
10   All night it fell, and when full inches seven
It lay in the depth of its uncompacted lightness,
The clouds blew off from a high and frosty heaven;
    And all woke earlier for the unaccustomed brightness
Of the winter dawning, the strange unheavenly glare:
15 The eye marvelled — marvelled at the dazzling whiteness;
    The ear hearkened* to the stillness of the solemn air;
No sound of wheel rumbling nor of foot falling,
And the busy morning cries came thin and spare.
    Then boys I heard, as they went to school, calling,
20 They gathered up the crystal manna** to freeze
Their tongues with tasting, their hands with snowballing;
    Or rioted in a drift, plunging up to the knees;
Or peering up from under the white-mossed wonder!'
'O look at the trees!' they cried, 'O look at the trees!'

Robert Bridges

* hearkened — *listened*
** manna — *food with spiritual blessing*

     98

1. Why is the snow described as moving "Stealthily" (line 3)?

   A   It falls silently.

   B   It falls in large flakes.

   C   It falls quickly.

   D   It falls evenly.

2. According to the poem, what effect does the snow have?

   A   It makes children behave badly.

   B   It makes it too cold to go outside.

   C   It makes the city quiet.

   D   It makes people reluctant to get out of bed.

3. Which of the following best describes how the snow falls?

   A   Slowly and gently

   B   Quickly and intermittently

   C   Sparsely and quietly

   D   Heavily and wildly

4. Which of the following statements is false?

   A   The snow makes everything in the city look the same.

   B   The snow falls during the night.

   C   The snow means more people went outside.

   D   The snow falls into every space available.

TURN OVER ➡

5. Why is the snow described as "veiling" (line 7)?

    A   Everything outside looks mysterious.

    B   Everything outside is concealed by the snow.

    C   Everything outside looks different.

    D   Everything outside is the same colour.

6. Which of the following would not be used to describe the snowfall?

    A   Deep

    B   Heavy

    C   Patchy

    D   Fresh

7. According to the poem, what causes people to wake up earlier than usual?

    A   They hear the noises of people in the snow.

    B   It is lighter outside because of the white snow.

    C   It is colder than normal.

    D   It is not as cloudy as it has been recently.

8. According to the poem, how do people react when they see the snow?

    A   They are amazed by what they see.

    B   They are annoyed at the inconvenience.

    C   They are unsettled by how quiet it is.

    D   They are shocked by its brightness.

9. Which of the following is not mentioned in the poem?

    A   In what part of the day the snowfall took place

    B   What parts of the day the poem is describing

    C   In which month the snowfall took place

    D   In which city the snowfall took place

10. Which of the following statements is false?

    A   Schoolboys threw snowballs.

    B   Schoolboys tasted the snow.

    C   Schoolboys shook the snow off tree branches.

    D   In places, the snow came up to the schoolboys' knees.

11. What does "unaccustomed" (line 13) mean?

    A   Unsurprising

    B   Unbelievable

    C   Unfamiliar

    D   Unwelcome

12. What does "crevices" (line 9) mean?

    A   Ditches

    B   Layers

    C   Gardens

    D   Gaps

END OF TEST

/ 12

You have **10 minutes** to do this test. Work as quickly and accurately as you can.

Read this passage carefully and answer the questions that follow.

School Uniform

   Some historians believe that it was during the sixteenth century that some
schoolchildren began wearing a prescribed outfit to school. Christ's Hospital, a
school in West Sussex, claims to have the oldest uniform that is still worn today.
Hardly altered in over 460 years, and introduced during the reign of its founder, King
5 Edward VI, all pupils don a blue coat, a white shirt and a leather belt. Boys also
wear breeches* and yellow socks, whilst girls put on a pleated skirt.
   In the year it was founded, Christ's Hospital welcomed 380 children from poor
London families. Girls were accepted, but they were in the minority. Generous
Londoners provided the pupils with the school's distinctive uniform, and this inspired
10 the nickname 'bluecoat schools' for these types of establishments.
   In 1870, the Elementary Education Act made education in England and Wales
more widely available for children aged 5 to 13, and so school uniforms became
more widespread over time. Nowadays, apart from a handful of schools like Christ's
Hospital, most items on a school kit list will look very similar up and down the
15 country.
   The advantages and disadvantages of school uniforms can be hot topics for
debate. Some believe uniforms can help to integrate pupils from different economic
backgrounds: those from less affluent families cannot be singled out at school based
on their attire. Uniforms can also give children a sense of unity and togetherness.
20 Conformity is a notion that is closely associated with any sort of uniform, and
people who oppose uniforms might argue that instructions on what to wear and
how to wear it prevent expressions of individuality. However, a loosened tie or
an untucked shirt can represent acts of disobedience that provide a glimpse of the
person behind the school badge.

* breeches — *short trousers*

1. When did King Edward VI reign?

   A   From 1413 to 1422

   B   From 1422 to 1461

   C   From 1547 to 1553

   D   From 1603 to 1625

2. According to the text, what distinguishes Christ's Hospital from all other schools?

   A   The bright yellow socks worn by its pupils.

   B   The belief that its pupils wear the country's oldest uniform.

   C   The fact that its uniform looks very different to modern school uniforms.

   D   The fact that it was the first school in the country to accept female pupils.

3. According to the text, what connection does Christ's Hospital have to the sixteenth century?

   A   The school follows a sixteenth-century curriculum.

   B   King Edward VI studied at the school.

   C   It has a uniform that was donated by King Edward VI.

   D   It has a uniform that was designed in the sixteenth century.

4. According to the text, which of the following cannot be true?

   A   When it opened, Christ's Hospital welcomed 300 boys.

   B   When it opened, Christ's Hospital welcomed 100 girls.

   C   When it opened, Christ's Hospital welcomed 190 girls.

   D   When it opened, Christ's Hospital welcomed 200 boys.

TURN OVER ➡

5. According to the text, which of the following best describes Christ's Hospital when it was founded?

A   It was a charity school.

B   It was an orphanage.

C   It was a boarding school.

D   It was a school for children who were unwell.

6. Why is it not surprising that uniforms became more commonplace from 1870 onwards?

A   School uniforms became more widely available.

B   It became the law to wear a school uniform.

C   More schools were established, so more children were seen in uniforms.

D   Attending school was made compulsory in Great Britain.

7. Which of the following best describes the Elementary Education Act?

A   A law which allowed poorer students to get an education.

B   A law which allowed students to start their education from a younger age.

C   A law which allowed older students to continue their education.

D   A law which allowed more students access to an education.

8. According to the text, which adjective describes the current school uniform at Christ's Hospital?

A   Sophisticated

B   Unremarkable

C   Unconventional

D   Inconspicuous

9. According to the text, which of the following is an advantage of school uniforms?

    A   They make it easier for pupils of a similar social standing to mix.

    B   They are stylish, so pupils who are less well-off are less likely to be bullied.

    C   They are affordable, which makes life easier for poorer pupils.

    D   They make all pupils seem equal, regardless of how wealthy they are.

10. According to the text, which of the following is given as a disadvantage of wearing a school uniform in accordance with school rules?

    A   It prevents pupils from revealing their true personality.

    B   It dictates how pupils should look.

    C   It encourages children to conform.

    D   It hinders freedom of speech.

11. The passage says "a loosened tie or an untucked shirt can represent acts of disobedience" (lines 22-23). This means that:

    A   detentions are handed out for not following the rules about school uniform.

    B   school rules are often relaxed about ties and shirts.

    C   ties and shirts never loosen and untuck themselves without assistance.

    D   defiant pupils may rearrange their shirts and ties.

12. According to the text, which is the most likely decade in which Christ's Hospital was founded?

    A   1450s

    B   1550s

    C   1650s

    D   It is not clear from the text.

END OF TEST

/ 12

You have **10 minutes** to do this test. Work as quickly and accurately as you can.

Read this passage carefully and answer the questions that follow.

An extract from 'The Railway Children'

They were not railway children to begin with. I don't suppose they had ever thought about railways except as a means of getting to Maskelyne and Cook's*, the Pantomime, Zoological Gardens, and Madame Tussaud's. They were just ordinary suburban children, and they lived with their Father and Mother in an ordinary
5   red-brick-fronted villa, with coloured glass in the front door, a tiled passage that was called a hall, a bath-room with hot and cold water, electric bells, French windows, and a good deal of white paint, and 'every modern convenience', as the house-agents say.

There were three of them. Roberta was the eldest. Of course, Mothers never have
10   favourites, but if their Mother HAD had a favourite, it might have been Roberta. Next came Peter, who wished to be an Engineer when he grew up; and the youngest was Phyllis, who meant extremely well.

Mother did not spend all her time in paying dull calls to dull ladies, and sitting dully at home waiting for dull ladies to pay calls to her. She was almost always there,
15   ready to play with the children, and read to them, and help them to do their home-lessons. Besides this she used to write stories for them while they were at school, and read them aloud after tea, and she always made up funny pieces of poetry for their birthdays and for other great occasions, such as the christening of the new kittens, or the refurnishing of the doll's house, or the time when they were
20   getting over the mumps.

These three lucky children always had everything they needed: pretty clothes, good fires, a lovely nursery with heaps of toys, and a Mother Goose wall-paper. They had a kind and merry nursemaid, and a dog who was called James, and who was their very own.

Edith Nesbit

* Maskelyne and Cook's — *a magical entertainment show*

Answer these questions about the text that you've just read.
Circle the letter that matches the correct answer.

1. According to the passage, where do the children live?
   A   Near a railway station
   B   In the centre of a small village
   C   On the edge of a town
   D   In the countryside

2. According to the passage, which of the following is true?
   A   The family own a dog called Peter.
   B   The family owns cats.
   C   There are six family members living in the house.
   D   The family lives close to the Zoological Gardens.

3. According to the passage, why are Roberta, Peter and Phyllis called the "railway children"?
   A   They frequently travel by train.
   B   Their mother tells them stories about railways.
   C   They talk about railways a lot.
   D   A reason is not given in the passage.

4. Who is the mother's favourite child?
   A   Roberta
   B   Peter
   C   Phyllis
   D   She does not have a favourite

TURN OVER ➡

5. Which of the following isn't mentioned as something the mother does?

    A   She helps her children write stories.

    B   She writes poetry for her children.

    C   She helps her children with their homework.

    D   She reads stories to her children.

6. Which of the following statements about the house is false?

    A   Some rooms in the house have open fires.

    B   The house has running water.

    C   The house is old-fashioned for its time.

    D   The house is made from bricks.

7. What is the author's opinion of the ladies that the mother visits?

    A   They are rude.

    B   They are uninteresting.

    C   They are always complaining.

    D   They aren't very clever.

8. According to the text, for which of the following occasions does the children's mother not write poetry?

    A   For the children's birthdays

    B   When the children are ill

    C   After the children have tea

    D   When the pets are christened

9. According to the passage, which of the following statements is false?

   A   Phyllis is younger than Roberta.

   B   Roberta has two siblings.

   C   Peter has two younger sisters.

   D   Phyllis has a brother.

10. Which of the following words best describes the mother?

   A   Sociable

   B   Proud

   C   Idle

   D   Creative

11. The passage says Phyllis "meant extremely well" (line 12). This means:

   A   Phyllis is good at explaining what things mean.

   B   Phyllis tries to do everything to the extreme.

   C   Phyllis is always friendly and polite.

   D   Phyllis tries to be helpful, but does not always succeed.

12. What does "convenience" (line 7) mean?

   A   Decoration

   B   Amenity

   C   Ornament

   D   Gadget

END OF TEST

/ 12

Time for a break! This puzzle will help you to practise your **vocabulary** and **logic** skills.

Word Search Riddler

Unscramble the eight anagrams to find a series of connected words.

Find these words in the word search below.

| **HOOCLS** |
| _____ |

| **NIMAEC** |
| _____ |

| **HOPS** |
| _____ |

| **SEMUMU** |
| _____ |

| **ONITATS** |
| _____ |

| **RAYBRLI** |
| _____ |

| **KAREBY** |
| _____ |

| **POTISLAH** |
| _____ |

Q	C	F	S	C	Y	S	N	N	Y	V	V	V	Y	R
X	A	J	R	Q	A	L	T	D	H	R	A	A	S	C
E	E	Q	I	V	P	U	I	A	A	J	E	G	D	H
L	A	T	I	P	S	O	H	B	T	C	Q	K	I	U
Q	T	E	S	U	O	H	G	A	R	I	L	Q	A	M
A	N	Q	R	U	Z	G	O	D	D	A	O	J	S	B
O	A	M	W	X	B	Z	Q	S	M	F	R	N	V	F
Q	R	C	I	N	E	M	A	U	H	C	M	Y	H	P
D	U	X	R	Q	L	Y	E	W	J	O	U	S	Q	D
Q	A	W	B	M	X	S	H	N	L	B	P	H	Z	D
M	T	N	E	E	U	R	J	U	A	O	I	G	A	D
T	S	T	F	M	N	W	U	C	F	K	O	S	Z	B
N	E	Q	Q	Y	M	J	B	Z	Q	G	P	H	E	W
H	R	J	F	Y	V	Y	N	H	Y	C	R	E	C	R
E	W	R	C	G	V	N	U	X	V	P	N	D	C	S

Once you have completed the word search, use one of the words to answer this riddle.

"Which building has the most stories?": _____

You have **10 minutes** to do this test. Work as quickly and accurately as you can.

Read this passage carefully and answer the questions that follow.

Archie and the Rollercoaster

Archie had always been shy. Where his brother, Charlie, was loud and raucous, Archie was quiet and reserved. Most people who knew him thought he was lonely and tried to force friends onto him, but Archie was perfectly happy in his own company. While he liked having people to play with, he didn't appreciate the
5   gesture.

In an attempt to encourage Archie to mingle with other children, Archie's parents had organised an unsupervised trip to the theme park with some children from the neighbourhood. Unluckily for Archie, it wasn't just the thought of making new friends that made him anxious. As he looked up at the towering structures, his
10 stomach tightened, and listening to the screams from the carriages that whizzed by made his palms sweat.

Although Charlie teased him for his cowardice, Archie was content to wait by the railings as the others dashed off to join the queue for the tallest rollercoaster in the park. He watched the park attendant measure the group to check that they were tall
15 enough to ride. As the attendant waved them through, Archie could hear Charlie boasting that he wanted to sit at the very front of the rollercoaster. Archie was a bit overwhelmed by the sheer number of people milling about near the ride, so he tucked himself out of the way, made himself comfortable on the pile of coats and bags and pulled out his book.

20 Fifteen minutes later, a shadow passed over Archie's book and he looked up to see Charlie standing over him.

"How was the rollercoaster?" asked Archie. Charlie just shook his head.

"I got to the front of the queue, but I couldn't go through with it." Archie smiled to himself; he and his brother were more alike than most people realised.

TURN OVER ➡

Answer these questions about the text that you've just read.
Circle the letter that matches the correct answer.

1. Why do people try to help Archie make friends?

    A   They do not want him to be picked on at school.

    B   They want him to be more like Charlie.

    C   They want him to be more sociable.

    D   They do not want him to feel isolated.

2. According to the passage, which of the following statements must be true?

    A   Archie does not know the other children very well.

    B   Charlie is Archie's only friend.

    C   Archie is lonely.

    D   Charlie is a bully.

3. Which of the following statements is true?

    A   Archie dislikes playing with others.

    B   Archie dislikes Charlie.

    C   Archie dislikes loud people.

    D   Archie dislikes other people forcing him to make friends.

4. Archie is "happy in his own company" (lines 3-4). This means:

    A   that he likes to be with his family.

    B   that he is comfortable being by himself.

    C   that he would rather be on his own.

    D   that he does not like to be with strangers.

5. Why do Archie's family organise a trip to the theme park?

    A   To help Archie overcome his fear of rollercoasters

    B   To encourage Charlie to meet new people

    C   To help Archie make new friends

    D   To encourage the brothers to spend more time together

6. Why doesn't Archie go on the rollercoaster with the other children?

    A   He is not tall enough.

    B   He doesn't want to spend time with the other members of the group.

    C   He is too scared.

    D   The other children have been teasing him.

7. According to the text, which of the following doesn't make Archie uneasy?

    A   Meeting new people

    B   Being by himself

    C   Large crowds

    D   Going on rollercoasters

8. Which of the following best describes Charlie?

    A   He is the bravest member of the group.

    B   He isn't as brave as he thinks he is.

    C   He is the most fun-loving member of the group.

    D   He is very similar to Archie.

TURN OVER ➡

9. According to the passage, which of the following statements must be true?

    A   Charlie is Archie's older brother.

    B   The other children in the group live near Charlie and Archie.

    C   Charlie sits at the front of the rollercoaster.

    D   Charlie isn't tall enough to ride the rollercoaster.

10. According to the passage, which of the following statements is false?

    A   Archie is happy to wait on his own.

    B   Charlie queues for the rollercoaster for a quarter of an hour.

    C   The brothers have more in common than people think.

    D   The brothers' parents accompany them on the trip.

11. What does "raucous" (line 1) mean?

    A   Irritating

    B   Sociable

    C   Rowdy

    D   Flamboyant

12. What does "anxious" (line 9) mean?

    A   Petrified

    B   Nauseous

    C   Nervous

    D   Miserable

END OF TEST

/ 12

You have **10 minutes** to do this test. Work as quickly and accurately as you can.

Read this passage carefully and answer the questions that follow.

Monkey Business

In the late 1960s, a young, female chimp named Washoe was part of a pioneering experiment. Although primates do not possess the physical capabilities for human speech, researchers wanted to discover whether Washoe could be taught American Sign Language (ASL). Washoe was chosen because of her age. As animals get older,
5 our ability to acquire language tends to reduce, so it was assumed that primates would behave in the same way.

Washoe lived with a human family and was raised in a similar way to a human child. In order to provide a focused learning environment, Washoe's family only ever communicated around her using ASL, never spoken language, and to avoid
10 invalidating the study they didn't teach Washoe around mealtimes.

Washoe was studied for approximately 13 years, and it's reported that she was the first non-human to learn ASL, understanding about 350 signs. Washoe spent her last 27 years at Central Washington University, before passing away in 2007.

Following the success of Project Washoe, researchers wanted to push the
15 boundaries even further and began a study with a male chimp called Nim. Project Nim, which began in 1973, shared many similarities with Project Washoe. When Project Nim ended in 1977, it was reported that Nim had learned around 125 signs, but some scientists put the actual number closer to 25.

A current study on primate language acquisition centres on Koko, a gorilla, who
20 was born in 1971. Koko has been taught ASL since the age of one, and she has since learned more than 1000 signs. Koko has also demonstrated evidence of linguistic creativity — she used the signs "finger" and "bracelet" when shown a ring.

However, not everyone has been convinced by the research. Critics claim that the primates only mimicked signs in order to obtain a food reward, and that they don't
25 actually understand the signs that they're using. They also believe that since the primates haven't shown any evidence of using grammar, they'll never truly be able to master human language.

TURN OVER ➡

Answer these questions about the text that you've just read.
Circle the letter that matches the correct answer.

1. According to the text, when is Washoe most likely to have lived?

   A   1971-2000

   B   1971-2007

   C   1965-2007

   D   1965-2000

2. Why do you think Washoe's family avoided teaching her around mealtimes?

   A   Because Washoe would be distracted by food

   B   Because they wanted to raise her in a similar way to a human child

   C   Because they wouldn't be able to sign and eat at the same time

   D   Because they didn't want her to associate learning ASL with food rewards

3. Why do you think Washoe's family never used spoken language around her?

   A   So Washoe could concentrate on learning ASL

   B   So the findings of their research were not invalidated

   C   So Washoe didn't feel like her family were excluding her from conversations

   D   So Washoe did not start using spoken language

4. According to the text, when did scientists stop studying Washoe?

   A   Approximately 1967

   B   Approximately 1970

   C   Approximately 1980

   D   Approximately 1994

5. Which of the following best describes Project Nim?
   - **A**   A study to see whether a chimp could learn ASL
   - **B**   A study to further the findings of Project Washoe
   - **C**   A study to replicate the findings of Project Washoe
   - **D**   A study to see if male chimps could learn ASL as effectively as females

6. Which of the following statements must be true?
   - **A**   There are many differences between Project Washoe and Project Nim.
   - **B**   Project Washoe was not as successful as Project Nim.
   - **C**   Nim and Washoe were alive at the same time.
   - **D**   Nim managed to learn over 125 signs.

7. According to the text, which of the following statements about Koko is true?
   - **A**   She has been learning sign language since 1971.
   - **B**   She continues to learn new signs.
   - **C**   She creates grammatical sentences using different signs.
   - **D**   She is able to sign the word "ring".

8. According to the text, which of the following statements is true?
   - **A**   Primates only use sign language as a means of getting food.
   - **B**   Primates will never be able to master human speech.
   - **C**   Primates will never be able to master grammar.
   - **D**   Research implies that chimps are better at learning ASL than gorillas.

TURN OVER ➡

9. Why do you think the researchers used young animals in their projects?

    A   Younger animals are easier to control.

    B   Younger animals are happier around humans.

    C   Younger animals are less likely to have health issues.

    D   Younger animals are better at language acquisition.

10. Which of the following best explains why each of the projects has taken place over several years?

    A   It takes at least fifteen years to learn a language.

    B   Primates are only able to learn a few signs each year.

    C   Language acquisition is a long-term process.

    D   Sign language is not as difficult to acquire as spoken language.

11. Which of the following statements must be false?

    A   Washoe was the first gorilla to learn ASL.

    B   Washoe spent almost three decades at Central Washington University.

    C   It has been suggested that primates do not understand ASL.

    D   The scientific community does not agree on the findings of these studies.

12. Why do you think the researchers chose to teach Nim ASL?

    A   ASL is used in many countries around the world.

    B   ASL is the easiest form of sign language to learn.

    C   ASL can be learnt by primates, whereas spoken language cannot.

    D   ASL was incredibly popular in the late 1960s and early 1970s.

END OF TEST

/ 12

You have **10 minutes** to do this test. Work as quickly and accurately as you can.

Read this passage carefully and answer the questions that follow.

How Not To Catch A Spy

The elderly man had been looking at his newspaper for the last half an hour, but he had not been reading it. To the unsuspecting eye, he was catching up on the latest world events, but I could tell otherwise. How does a man read a newspaper without moving his eyes? It was all pretence; I just didn't know why.

5   I imagined he was a private investigator. The old-fashioned methods are undoubtedly the best. I have a nostalgic love for spy thrillers from the 1960s, with their retro gadgets, over-the-top acting and dated charm. I was almost certain he would have a walkie-talkie underneath his newspaper, or a secret camera in his shirt.

His age was another factor; surely nobody would suspect an elderly man of such 10 an enterprise. It was similar to using children as spies: they could go unnoticed in any crowd.

I needed to know the truth. I walked past him, glancing casually over the newspaper at his glassy-eyed stare. After a short time, I turned around and walked behind the bench at a discreet distance. To my surprise, I saw no gadgets, no secret 15 radio, not even a notepad.

My suspicion reached fever pitch, so I picked up a nearby ball and rolled it towards the bench. The man didn't move an inch. It was most unnatural behaviour and warranted an explanation. I walked over to the bench and gave a slight cough.

"Excuse me, sir, do you mind if I borrow your newspaper?" I asked.

20 "Oh yes," said the man, "I don't actually need it, you see. I am old and my eyesight is poor, but I rather enjoy the sounds of the park. It's just a prop to help me blend in, but I suppose someone should actually read it."

As he waved the newspaper in my direction, I felt my face flush.

"No sir, that's perfectly fine, I'm sorry to have bothered you." I turned and walked 25 away, realising that I needed to stop watching so many spy films.

TURN OVER ➡

Answer these questions about the text that you've just read.
Circle the letter that matches the correct answer.

1. Which of the following statements must be true?

    A   The elderly man is not reading the newspaper.

    B   The elderly man does not know about the latest world events.

    C   The elderly man gets no use out of the newspaper.

    D   The elderly man was once a private investigator.

2. Which of the following makes the narrator initially suspicious of the elderly man?

    A   The elderly man is reading a newspaper in a public place.

    B   The elderly man doesn't react when the ball rolls towards him.

    C   Elderly people are renowned for being spies.

    D   He thinks the elderly man is pretending to read a newspaper.

3. The narrator has a "nostalgic love for spy thrillers from the 1960s" (line 6). This means:

    A   He is embarrassed to admit he watches spy thrillers from the 1960s.

    B   He thinks that newer spy films do not have as many thrills in them.

    C   Old-fashioned spy films bring back happy memories.

    D   He enjoys talking about 60s spy films with older people.

4. According to the text, why does the narrator enjoy spy thrillers from the 1960s?

    1. Because of the exaggerated acting
    2. Because they have better plots than modern spy films
    3. Because of the old-fashioned gadgets
    4. Because of the charming actors

    A   1 and 2

    B   2 and 3

    C   1 and 3

    D   2 and 4

5. According to the text, why would an elderly person make a good spy?

    A   Elderly people are less likely to arouse suspicion.

    B   Elderly people are more enterprising.

    C   Elderly people have more life experience.

    D   Elderly people make just as good spies as children.

6. Why does the speaker roll a ball towards the elderly man's bench?

    A   To scare him

    B   To prevent him from reading his newspaper

    C   To see how he will react

    D   To surprise him

7. According to the text, which of the following statements must be true?

    A   The elderly man is lonely.

    B   The elderly man has been reading for over an hour.

    C   The elderly man enjoys spy films from the 1960s.

    D   The newspaper helps the elderly man go unnoticed.

8. Why does the speaker ask to borrow the elderly man's newspaper?

    A   To read it for himself

    B   To see if there are any gadgets hidden behind it

    C   To expose the elderly man as a criminal

    D   To discover why the elderly man is using it

TURN OVER ➡

9. Which of the following best describes how the narrator feels after confronting the elderly man?

   A   Ashamed

   B   Relieved

   C   Content

   D   Bemused

10. Which of the following best describes the speaker's conclusion at the end of the text?

   A   That he watches too many films

   B   That his love of spy films has made him too suspicious of people

   C   That he feels embarrassed

   D   That he feels guilty for bothering the elderly man

11. What does "pretence" (line 4) mean?

   A   Disguise

   B   Deception

   C   Cheating

   D   Treachery

12. What does "undoubtedly" (line 6) mean?

   A   Unbelievably

   B   Apparently

   C   Definitely

   D   Arguably

END OF TEST

/ 12

Time for a break! These puzzles are a great way to practise your **word** and **logic** skills.

Word Ladders

Can you get from the top word to the bottom word by only changing one letter of each word at a time?

The first one has been done for you.

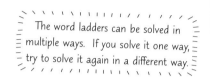

The word ladders can be solved in multiple ways. If you solve it one way, try to solve it again in a different way.

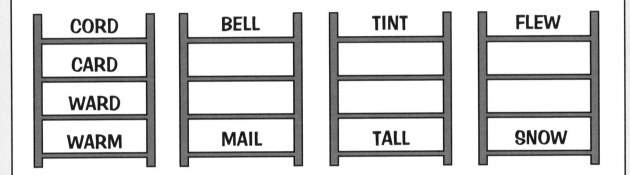

CORD	BELL	TINT	FLEW
CARD			
WARD			
WARM	MAIL	TALL	SNOW

What Am I?

Use the clues to work out which word is being described.

The first letter of each answer has been given for you.

I can be written in capital letters forwards, backwards, or upside down, and still be read from left to right. *(My first letter is N)*

What am I? _____

I am a five-letter word that sits beneath you. *(My first letter is C)*

If you take away my first letter, I am on you.

If you take away my first and second letters, I am all around you.

What am I? _____

---

(10)

You have **10 minutes** to do this test. Work as quickly and accurately as you can.

Read this passage carefully and answer the questions that follow.

An extract from 'The Adventures of Tom Sawyer'

About half-past ten the cracked bell of the small church began to ring, and presently the people began to gather for the morning sermon. The Sunday-school children distributed themselves about the house and occupied pews with their parents, so as to be under supervision. Aunt Polly came, and Tom and Sid and Mary

5 sat with her — Tom being placed next the aisle, in order that he might be as far away from the open window and the seductive outside summer scenes as possible. The crowd filed up the aisles: the aged and needy postmaster, who had seen better days; the mayor and his wife — for they had a mayor there, among other unnecessaries; the justice of the peace; the Widow Douglas, fair, smart, and forty, a generous,

10 good-hearted soul and well-to-do, her hill mansion the only palace in the town, and the most hospitable and much the most lavish in the matter of festivities that St. Petersburg could boast; the bent and venerable* Major and Mrs. Ward; lawyer Riverson, the new notable from a distance; next the belle of the village, followed by a troop of lawn-clad** and ribbon-decked young heart-breakers; then all the young

15 clerks in town in a body — for they had stood in the vestibule sucking their cane-heads***, a circling wall of oiled and simpering admirers, till the last girl had run their gauntlet****; and last of all came the Model Boy, Willie Mufferson, taking as heedful care of his mother as if she were cut glass. He always brought his mother to church, and was the pride of all the matrons. The boys all hated him, he was so

20 good. And besides, he had been "thrown up to them"***** so much. His white handkerchief was hanging out of his pocket behind, as usual on Sundays — accidentally. Tom had no handkerchief, and he looked upon boys who had as snobs.

Mark Twain

* venerable — *respected because of age*
** lawn-clad — *wearing linen*
*** cane-heads — *tops of walking sticks*

**** run their gauntlet — *go through a difficult or*
humiliating experience
***** thrown up to them — *held up as an example of goodness*

Answer these questions about the text that you've just read.
Circle the letter that matches the correct answer.

1. According to the passage, why do the children sit next to their parents?

    A   Because their parents need to watch over them

    B   Because the children need to learn how to behave by watching their parents

    C   Because their parents have saved them a place

    D   Because they want to keep their parents company

2. Which of the following is not mentioned in the passage?

    A   What time of day it is

    B   What day of the week it is

    C   What month of the year it is

    D   Which season it is

3. Which of the following statements is true?

    A   The church is very spacious.

    B   Willie Mufferson is popular with his peers.

    C   The mayor and his wife live in a hill mansion.

    D   The church bell is damaged.

4. What does the narrator think about the mayor?

    A   He isn't needed.

    B   He is a vital member of the community.

    C   He is fair and just.

    D   He helps to keep the peace.

TURN OVER ➡

5. According to the passage, which of the following statements about Widow Douglas are true?

    1. She is wealthy.
    2. She is the best host in St. Petersburg.
    3. She lives in one of the biggest palaces in town.
    4. She is boastful.

    A   1 and 2

    B   2 and 3

    C   1 and 3

    D   2 and 4

6. According to the text, why is Tom seated next to the aisle?

    A   So his view is not disrupted by someone in front of him.

    B   So he is not distracted by the view outside.

    C   So he isn't near the draught from the open window.

    D   Because the Sunday-school children have to sit with their parents.

7. According to the passage, what are the young clerks doing in the vestibule?

    A   Standing aimlessly with their walking sticks

    B   Huddled in a circle admiring themselves

    C   Waiting for everyone else to find their seats

    D   Looking at the young ladies as they come into church

8. Why is Willie Mufferson called the "Model Boy" (line 17)?

    A   Because he is well-behaved and polite

    B   Because he is good-looking

    C   Because all the other boys want to be like him

    D   Because all the other boys want to be liked by him

9. Willie Mufferson looks after his mother "as if she were cut glass" (line 18). This suggests:

    A   he thinks she has a sharp tongue.

    B   he thinks she is dangerous to others.

    C   he thinks she is very fragile.

    D   she is very clumsy.

10. According to the passage, what does Tom think about boys who have handkerchiefs?

    A   They look silly with them hanging out from their pockets.

    B   They think they are better than him.

    C   They are not as good as him.

    D   He wishes he was more like them.

11. What does "lavish" (line 11) mean?

    A   Boisterous

    B   Expensive

    C   Colourful

    D   Extravagant

12. What does "simpering" (line 16) mean?

    A   Smirking

    B   Preening

    C   Laughing

    D   Swooning

END OF TEST

/ 12

You have **10 minutes** to do this test. Work as quickly and accurately as you can.

Read this passage carefully and answer the questions that follow.

Kinderzeche

Dinkelsbühl is a quaint town in Bavaria, Germany. In the middle of July, commencing on a Friday, Dinkelsbühlers and visitors alike celebrate an annual ten-day festival known as Kinderzeche. Kinderzeche honours the children of Dinkelsbühl, who saved the town from being destroyed by Swedish forces in the

5 seventeenth century.

The events of 1632 remain unsubstantiated. However, hearsay has it that during the Thirty Years' War, which began in 1618, a Swedish commander called Colonel Sperreuth threatened to ransack Dinkelsbühl. The town council met to agree how to act. At the meeting, a gatekeeper's daughter offered to gather together the town's

10 children and appeal to Sperreuth for mercy. She carried out her plan, the Colonel's heart softened and he spared the town, with the words that Dinkelsbühl should not forget the debt owed to its children.

This story is celebrated every year in a fixed format which Kinderzeche fans know off by heart. On consecutive Sundays, the historical Kinderzeche procession goes

15 through the town: over 1000 men, women and children (and even some four-legged friends), don traditional attire and march to the sound of brass instruments. A day later, this procession takes place again, but school classes also join in. On Tuesday, the procession is smaller — only children take part.

Experienced onlookers find themselves a good position from which to watch

20 these events, and some arrive armed with flowers and goodie bags to hand out to those walking past in historical garb. Crowds cheer at the sight of red and white Dinkelsbühl flags and boo at those dressed as Colonel Sperreuth and his men.

Answer these questions about the text that you've just read.
Circle the letter that matches the correct answer.

1. Which day of the week marks the end of Kinderzeche?

    A   Saturday

    B   Friday

    C   Monday

    D   Sunday

2. What is Kinderzeche?

    A   A festival that marks the end of the Thirty Years' War

    B   A festival that celebrates the gatekeeper's daughter

    C   A festival that commemorates the children of Dinkelsbühl

    D   A festival that pays tribute to Bavaria

3. According to the text, when did the Swedes seize Dinkelsbühl?

    A   Fourteen years after the start of the Thirty Years' War

    B   In the sixteenth century

    C   Sixty-nine years before the turn of the eighteenth century

    D   In the 1700s

4. Why were the Swedes merciful to Dinkelsbühl?

    A   Because the gatekeeper's daughter assembled the town's children

    B   Because the town council begged for mercy

    C   Because the sight of the town's children asking for compassion was touching

    D   Because Colonel Sperreuth was indebted to Dinkelsbühl's children

TURN OVER ➡

5. Why could the structure of Kinderzeche be described as rigid?

    A   It never changes.

    B   It is a faithful catalogue of historical events.

    C   It occurs every 12 months.

    D   It is organised with military precision.

6. According to the text, how many times does the historical procession take place during Kinderzeche?

    A   Twice

    B   Three times

    C   Four times

    D   Five times

7. On which days would you find children in a Kinderzeche procession?

    A   Sunday, Monday and Tuesday

    B   Just Monday and Tuesday

    C   Just Sunday and Monday

    D   Sunday, Friday and Tuesday

8. According to the text, which of the following statements must be true?

    A   The town provides participants with seventeenth-century clothing.

    B   Adults sometimes take part in the historical processions.

    C   Crowds won't be able to watch the historical procession on a Monday.

    D   Kinderzeche is a public holiday.

9. The best vantage points for viewing the Kinderzeche events are likely to be taken by:

    A   those who have been to Kinderzeche before.

    B   people wearing costumes.

    C   children.

    D   historians.

10. What could be described as a perk of taking part in the processions?

    A   Participants miss three days of school.

    B   Participants learn about the Thirty Years' War.

    C   Participants may be given gifts.

    D   Participants are forewarned about changes to the schedule.

11. Which of the following is not mentioned in the text?

    A   Why Swedish forces attacked Dinkelsbühl

    B   On which day school classes form part of the historical procession

    C   How often Kinderzeche takes place

    D   Who was in charge of the Swedish forces

12. Which of the following statements is not mentioned in the text?

    A   Animals take part in the historical procession.

    B   Some participants dress as Swedish soldiers.

    C   The Dinkelsbühl flag is a red cross on a white background.

    D   The historical procession takes place to music.

END OF TEST

/ 12

You have **10 minutes** to do this test. Work as quickly and accurately as you can.

Read this passage carefully and answer the questions that follow.

An extract from 'Journey to the Centre of the Earth'

Supper was rapidly devoured, and the little company housed themselves as best they could. The bed was hard, the shelter not very substantial, and our position an anxious one, at five thousand feet above the sea level. Yet I slept particularly well; it was one of the best nights I had ever had, and I did not even dream.

5   Next morning we awoke half frozen by the sharp keen air, but with the light of a splendid sun. I rose from my granite bed and went out to enjoy the magnificent spectacle that lay unrolled before me.

I stood on the very summit of the southernmost of Snæfell's* peaks. The range of the eye extended over the whole island. By an optical law** which obtains at

10   all great heights, the shores seemed raised and the centre depressed. It seemed as if one of Helbesmer's raised maps*** lay at my feet. I could see deep valleys intersecting each other in every direction, precipices like low walls, lakes reduced to ponds, rivers abbreviated into streams. On my right were numberless glaciers and innumerable peaks, some plumed with feathery clouds of smoke. The undulating

15   surface of these endless mountains, crested with sheets of snow, reminded one of a stormy sea. If I looked westward, there the ocean lay spread out in all its magnificence, like a mere continuation of those flock-like summits. The eye could hardly tell where the snowy ridges ended and the foaming waves began.

I was thus steeped in the marvellous ecstasy which all high summits develop in

20   the mind; and now without giddiness, for I was beginning to be accustomed to these sublime aspects of nature. My dazzled eyes were bathed in the bright flood of the solar rays.

Jules Verne

* Snæfell — *a volcano in Iceland*
** optical law — *illusion*
*** Helbesmer's raised maps — *maps that are three dimensional*

1. Which of the following statements is false?

    A   The narrator did not dream that night.

    B   The poor conditions made it hard for the narrator to sleep.

    C   The company are high up in the mountains.

    D   The company were not well protected from the elements.

2. According to the text, why is the position of the campsite an "anxious one" (line 3)?

    A   The air temperature is dangerously low.

    B   It is poorly protected from the weather.

    C   It is high up a mountainside.

    D   There is not enough room for the whole group.

3. Which of the following best describes the company's camp?

    A   Uncomfortable and barely sufficient

    B   Comfortable but basic

    C   Solid and rocky

    D   Leaky and uneven

4. Which of the following statements is true?

    A   The company wake up to a cold morning.

    B   The company wake up to a warm, sunny day.

    C   The company wake up with frostbite.

    D   The company wake up at dawn.

TURN OVER ➡

5. Which of the following can the narrator not see from the peak?

   A   The shoreline

   B   A mountain range

   C   Ponds

   D   Glaciers

6. Why does the narrator describe the landscape as being like a map?

   A   He had seen it on a map earlier that day.

   B   He is high up and looking down on the land.

   C   He has a map at his feet.

   D   From his perspective the land looks flat.

7. The narrator says rivers became "abbreviated into streams" (line 13).
   This means:

   A   that the rivers flow into streams.

   B   that the rivers are shorter than the streams.

   C   that the rivers appear as small as streams.

   D   that the narrator can only see streams.

8. Which of the following statements is true?

   A   The narrator struggles to differentiate between mountains and the ocean.

   B   There are lots of people in the company.

   C   The company do not enjoy their supper.

   D   The company are on the northern side of Snæfell.

9. What reason does the narrator give for being able to calmly appreciate the view?

 A He is not afraid of heights.

 B The sun is in his eyes, so he cannot see the drop.

 C He is suffering from altitude sickness and is beginning to hallucinate.

 D He is starting to get more used to the amazing sights.

10. Which of the following best describes the island?

 A The island has snow-capped mountains.

 B The island is small and easily navigated.

 C The island is shaped like a crater.

 D The island is mountainous around the edges.

11. What does "innumerable" (line 14) mean?

 A Countless

 B Not many

 C Several

 D Unusual

12. What does "undulating" (line 14) mean?

 A Changing

 B Wave-like

 C Sharp

 D Unbroken

END OF TEST

/ 12

Time for a break! This puzzle is a great way to practise your **logic** skills.

Pet Puzzler

Mike, Josh and Clara are all different ages, and they have all recently adopted a pet. They have also bought their pets a coloured toy each to keep them happy and amused.

Using the clues and the table below, can you work out how old each person is, which pet they have adopted and what colour toy they bought for their pet?

Fill in the table using ticks ✓ and crosses ✗ to show what is true and what is false.

The first clue has been done for you as an example. Because the rabbit belongs to the youngest person (12), and the dog belongs to the eldest person (16), we can then tell the cat belongs to the 14 year old.

It may help to return to earlier clues when you have added new information to the table.

		AGE			TOY			PET		
		12	14	16	RED	BLUE	WHITE	CAT	DOG	RABBIT
NAME	MIKE									
	JOSH									
	CLARA									
PET	CAT	✗	✓	✗						
	DOG	✗	✗	✓						
	RABBIT	✓	✗	✗						
TOY	RED									
	BLUE									
	WHITE									

Clue 1: The youngest person adopted a rabbit, and the eldest person adopted a dog.

Clue 2: The red toy does not belong to Clara or the rabbit.

Clue 3: The dog was given a blue toy.

Clue 4: Josh purchased the white toy.

When you're sure of a fact, add it to the sentences below:

Mike is .... years old, and bought a .... toy for his ....

Josh is .... years old, and bought a .... toy for his ....

Clara is .... years old, and bought a .... toy for her ....

VCXPDE2

CGP

11+ Verbal Reasoning
Comprehension

Or the **CEM** test

10-Minute Tests
Answer Book

Ages
10-11

Test 1 — pages 2-5

1. A
Lines 1-2 state that when Pip was a child, he could not say his full name or anything clearer than the sound "Pip".

2. B
Line 1 states that Pip's "family name" (last name) is Pirrip, and his "Christian name" (first name) is Philip. Therefore, his full name is Philip Pirrip.

3. B
"on the authority of" (line 4) means 'from a reliable source' which suggests that Pip believes the inscription on his father's tombstone must be correct.

4. D
Although line 9 states that Pip believes his father was a "square, stout, dark man, with curly black hair", in lines 5-6 Pip admits "I never saw my father ... and never saw any likeness of either of them", so it cannot be clear from the text.

5. A
Line 10 states that Georgiana is the wife of Pip's father. In the next line, Pip refers to his "mother", therefore, it can be assumed that Georgiana is Pip's mother.

6. B
In line 10, Pip describes how he uses the font style ("character and turn") of her tombstone's inscription to imagine what she looks like. Therefore, Pip believes she was freckled and sickly because of the style of the writing on her tombstone.

7. D
If something is "universal" then everybody can relate to it. Therefore, a "universal struggle" is something that everyone experiences. In this case, Pip is referring to life.

8. C
Line 5 states that Pip has a sister — "Mrs. Joe Gargery". Therefore, he is not the last surviving member of his family.

9. C
Line 5 states that Pip's sister married the blacksmith, and that her name is "Mrs. Joe Gargery". Lines 11-13 tell us that Pip has five brothers buried in the churchyard. However, the passage does not state Pip's father's first name.

10. B
To do something "religiously" means 'to do something constantly'. 'To entertain' an idea is 'to think about it'.

11. A
"raw" means 'cold'.

12. D
"bleak" means 'desolate'.

Test 2 — pages 6-9

1. B
Lines 2-3 state that Cross "was about to clock off when he received the call", which means that he was about to leave work when the call came through.

2. B
Line 6 states that the burglaries are "seemingly unconnected" which suggests that they have been committed by different people.

3. D
Line 8 states that Inspector Cross "had been in the force for most of his working life". Lines 22-23 state that Cross takes "a brief pause from the intensity of his job". The word "intensity" suggests that his job is demanding.

4. C
Line 7 says the "increased workload" is making Cross "grumble". This suggests that the changing amount of work is making Cross grumpy.

5. D
Lines 9-10 state that Inspector Cross wants to go on a world cruise with his wife, have lazy breakfasts on the patio, and get a dog.

6. B
Lines 11-12 state that Inspector Cross goes to the shop because his stomach is "grumbling", therefore he is hungry.

7. C
To 'radiate' means 'to emit light'. Therefore, the light appears to be coming from inside the food.

8. C
Lines 17-18 state that "the moon had appeared from behind a cloud". Therefore, it can be assumed that earlier it was hidden behind the cloud.

9. C
Lines 15-16 state that it had been "ten minutes since he had received the call". Line 20 states that Cross has "twenty minutes left" until he has to be at the crime scene. Therefore, he has 30 minutes after receiving the call to arrive at the crime scene.

10. B
Lines 21-23 describe Inspector Cross sitting on a bench looking at the moon, "taking a brief pause from the intensity of his job". This suggests that looking at the moon helps to calm him.

11. D
"renowned" means 'well-known'.

12. A
"luminous" means 'bright'.

Puzzles 1 — page 10

Synonym Search

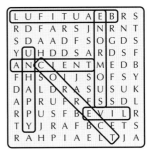

2

Spelling Bee

Bee's Favourite Flower: Tulip

Test 3 — pages 11-14

1. D
Line 1 states that Buñol is a town in Valencia, Spain.

2. B
Although line 5 states that some people believe the festival started when "a food fight broke out among friends", the origins of the festival "remain mysterious" (line 4) and so it is not clear where the idea came from.

3. B
Line 8 states that the town "struggled to accommodate so many guests", suggesting Buñol could not cope with the number of visitors. Because of this, the festival is now "limited to 20 000 people", all of whom must "have a ticket" (lines 8-9).

4. A
Line 7 states that prior to 2013 "between 30 000 and 50 000 people took part each year", but since 2013 the festival has been "limited to 20 000 people" (lines 8-9). Therefore, there could not have been more participants in 2013 than 2012.

5. B
"batten down the hatches" means to protect a building from something. Therefore, shopkeepers try to protect their property during the festival.

6. C
The "sea of red slush" is the mass of squashed tomatoes thrown during the festival.

7. B
Lines 14-15 refer to "the water cannon used to signal the start of the festival". Therefore, a cannon firing signals the start of the festival.

8. A
Lines 15-16 state that when the cannon fires again "the tomato throwing stops".

9. C
Line 18 states that nobody is allowed to "bring anything that could potentially injure another person". Therefore, items that could harm others are prohibited.

10. B
Although lines 19-20 state that revellers are "encouraged to wear protective goggles and gloves", they are not provided with them.

11. C
"squandered" means 'to waste something', therefore a lot of tomatoes are wasted during the festival.

12. A
"Revellers" are 'people who celebrate an event'.

Test 4 — pages 15-18

1. B
"neglected" means 'ignored'. Since shade has neglected the narrator's face, this means he has not been in the shade for a while, so this suggests he spends a lot of time outdoors.

2. D
Line 8 states that the fish are travelling to the "depths below", which suggests they are at the bottom of the lake and the boy cannot see them.

3. A
Lines 9-14 describe the sun submerging itself into the water as though it is lowering itself directly into the lake.

4. C
Line 1 states that the lake is "empty". Therefore, there cannot be other boats on the lake.

5. C
Lines 17-20 describe the sunset being reflected in the water — the lake is described as being "set ablaze". At the same time, the boy touches the surface of the water, causing it to ripple. Therefore 2 and 3 occur simultaneously.

6. B
Lines 21-23 state that the sunlight has "almost gone", referring to it as "the day's last sacrifice" (line 24).

7. B
Although the sunset is described as "orange" on line 15, it is describing the light from the sun rather than the water. Elsewhere, the water is described as "gold" (line 2), "purple" (line 27) and "silver" (line 36).

8. C
Although line 26 states that the boy's eyes "start to close", he is still awake when the moon comes out on line 28 because he does not lay "down his head" to fall asleep until line 34.

9. D
The "golden surface" (line 17) refers to the surface of the water. In line 2, the boat is described as being reflected in "precious gold".

10. D
Lines 37-40 describe how the man thinks that his son is more precious than anything else — he does not even compare to the man's "precious" boat.

11. B
"submerging" means 'immersing'.

12. D
"wan" means 'pale'.

Puzzles 2 — page 19

Compound-Word Chain

jelly — fish — bowl

time — table — spoon

horse — shoe — lace

light — house — work

Anagram Anacondas

YNOHTP — PYTHON

IPVSER — VIPERS

Test 5 — pages 20-23

1.   B
The phrase 'my memory is playing tricks on me' can be a way of saying that you can't remember something. This suggests that the narrator's memory isn't as good as it used to be.

2.   C
Line 3 states that the narrator is the "youngster" of the party.

3.   D
Line 4 gives "experience, character, knowledge" as qualities that make up a man, but self-confidence is not mentioned.

4.   B
To 'warm at the thought' can mean 'to flush'. Although this could be interpreted as embarrassment, in lines 5-6, the narrator says he was "coming into my own". This means that the narrator is starting to gain the trust and respect of his colleagues, the thought of which has made him flush with pride.

5.   C
"the pride which goes before a fall" is a phrase which means 'being overconfident can sometimes lead to mistakes'.

6.   A
"exhilarated" means "excited". Line 10 states that sleep seemed impossible because the narrator was "unduly excited".

7.   A
Lines 13-14 state that Lord John was "wrapped in the South American poncho", not Summerlee.

8.   B
Lines 15-16 state that the "full moon was shining" and that the air was "cold". It is not a quiet night because Challenger's snores "reverberated through the woods".

9.   D
Lines 18-19 describe how the narrator intends to return with a "record" of his visit to the central lake, and he hopes the others will consider him an "even more worthy associate".

10.   B
Line 3 states that the narrator is the youngest in the group. Lines 16-17 suggest the narrator is impulsive — the thought of the walk came "suddenly" and the fact that he acted upon his sudden thought suggests he can be impulsive.

11.   A
"Stole" can mean 'to move quietly and inconspicuously'.

12.   B
"Associate" means 'companion'.

Test 6 — pages 24-27

1.   B
Line 2 states that Timbuktu is remote, and lines 3-6 state that Timbuktu takes a long time to get to. This suggests that Timbuktu is isolated.

2.   D
Lines 2-3 state that Timbuktu is a city in a West African country. Therefore, Timbuktu is in Africa.

3.   C
Lines 5-6 state that Timbuktu is situated on "the southern edge of the Sahara Desert". Therefore, the Sahara Desert is located to the north of Timbuktu.

4.   B
Lines 7-9 state that early settlements were established in Timbuktu because the River Niger "provided water and grazing land".

5.   A
Line 11 states that the Niger River was "used for transporting goods".

6.   D
Line 12 states that in the fourteenth century (the 1300s), trade in salt was "thriving". "Thriving" means 'flourishing'.

7.   B
"a hive of intellectual activity" suggests that there were a lot of intellectuals in Timbuktu, making it a busy and important place of learning.

8.   C
Line 14 states that the manuscripts were "imported to Timbuktu" and line 15 states that some texts came from Egypt. Therefore, the manuscripts can be described as 'foreign'.

9.   A
Lines 15-16 state that scholars who made pilgrimages to Mecca sometimes copied texts to take back to their own libraries, therefore pilgrims would be the most likely option.

10.   D
Line 17 states that "personal libraries were prevalent among Timbuktu's scholarly elite". Since the elite represents only a small proportion of society, not all inhabitants of Timbuktu would have owned their own library.

11.   D
Line 22 states that the Institute was named "in honour of Baba". To name something in honour of someone is a sign of respect.

12.   B
"prevalent" means 'widespread'.

Test 7 — pages 28-31

1.   A
Line 1 states that Mrs. Darling "loved to have everything just so". This means she has a exact and particular way of doing things.

2.   B
Lines 1-2 state that Mr. Darling had a "passion for being exactly like his neighbours". Therefore, because his neighbours have nurses, the family has to get a nurse.

3.   A
Line 3 states that the Darling family is "poor", so they can't afford a human nurse.

4.   D
Line 3 says that the family were poor "owing to the amount of milk the children drank".

5. D

Line 20 states that the nursery couldn't be conducted "more correctly", suggesting that Nana is very competent.

6. C

In this context, "charges" means 'someone who is committed to someone's care'. Therefore Nana's charges are the Darling children.

7. C

"no patience" means to have 'no sympathy for', which suggests that sometimes Nana has no sympathy for the children because she knows when they are faking illnesses.

8. A

Line 11 states that Nana's kennel is located in the nursery; since "nursery" is another world for 'a child's bedroom', Nana sleeps in the same room as the children.

9. D

Lines 9 and 10 refer to Nana bathing the children, lines 15-16 refer to her taking them to school, and lines 11-13 refer to her looking after the children when they are sick. Therefore the answer is all of the above.

10. A

Line 21 mentions that Mr. Darling worries that the neighbours "talked". Line 20 states that Nana runs the nursery correctly, so it must be the fact that Nana is a dog that worries Mr. Darling.

11. B

"engage" someone in this context means 'to hire'. The Darlings have hired Nana as their nurse.

12. C

"sedately" means 'calmly'.

Puzzles 3 — page 32

Test 8 — pages 33-36

1. D

Lines 1-2 state that writing a novel is like "a builder trying to build a house".

2. A

Line 3 states that the writer only wishes to finish a novel even if it "fell apart at the end".

3. B

Line 5 states the narrator's parents told her writing "wasn't a stable career". This suggests that they are practical and realistic.

4. B

In line 6, the writer says her book is "nonexistent" which suggests that she is not 'good enough' to prove her parents wrong.

5. B

Lines 9-10 explain how the writer takes inspiration from "people walking the streets", including their "individual quirks" and differences.

6. C

Line 12 states that Dickens is a master of "turning the mundane into the fascinating". This suggests that she admires how Dickens is able to make any anything appear interesting.

7. D

In line 15, the writer says that "true stories are the most far-fetched". This suggests that even though the biographies of rock stars are based on the truth, they are almost unbelievable.

8. A

Lines 8-9 state that the main problem the writer has is having "an idea good enough to sustain an entire novel".

9. D

Line 20 says that "the best authors merge style and substance in their books".

10. C

Line 19 says that books with a "great plot" sometimes "fly off the shelves", suggesting that they sell faster than well-written stories.

11. A

"sustain" means 'support'.

12. D

"alchemy" means 'the process of changing something basic into an object of value'.

Test 9 — pages 37-40

1. C

Lines 1-2 state that coffee is "big business" because "around two billion cups" of coffee are consumed each day.

2. A

Lines 2-3 state that Brazil is the world leader when it comes to the "quantity of coffee produced".

3. D

Lines 3-4 tell us that the USA "imports the most coffee"; therefore Finland must import less coffee than America.

4. A

Line 9 states that the berries contain seeds. Therefore, as a peaberry is a seed, a peaberry is found inside a berry.

5. D

A jury is a group of people who decide something; if they are "still out" it means they have not come to a decision. Therefore, coffee drinkers haven't decided if they prefer the taste of regular coffee or peaberry.

6. D
Line 14 states that in the dry method the berries are "left to dry outside for up to four weeks". This is better in drier countries as the berries require dry heat.

7. A
Lines 15-16 state that the wet method "requires machinery to pulp, ferment and wash the berries", and so requires more equipment than the dry method.

8. B
Lines 19-20 explain that the beans are kept in constant motion during roasting "to avoid scorching".

9. D
Lines 22-23 state that instant coffee is quicker to brew than the other types of coffee.

10. B
Line 18 mentions that the coffee bean develops a dark brown colour during roasting. Line 9 mentions that the berries take around "nine months to ripen". Line 10 mentions that a peaberry develops in around "5% of cases". However, which method of processing gives the most flavour is not mentioned.

11. A
"connoisseurs" can mean 'experts'.

12. D
"distinctive" means 'recognisable'.

Test 10 — pages 41-44

1. A
Line 1 describes the sweet shop as "quaint". This means that it has an old-fashioned charm.

2. D
Line 1 states that Brian sees a couple picnicking by a stream; line 4 states that he has seen "grey tower blocks" (high-rise buildings); and congested roads (congested means 'clogged with traffic'). However, the text does not mention a lake.

3. A
Line 4 states that Brian is travelling north. This suggests he must live south of the Yorkshire Dales.

4. C
Line 10 states that Lucy initially thought her move to the countryside "had been a mistake", but lines 10-13 suggest that she is beginning to enjoy various aspects of country life.

5. C
Lines 11-12 state that Lucy enjoys the country air "above all".

6. D
Line 15 states that Brian believes "rural life was no match for city living". Therefore, he does not secretly want to move to the countryside.

7. C
A "city slicker" is someone who is used to an urban lifestyle. "reformed" means 'changed', so Lucy has changed her city way of life.

8. B
Lines 8-9 state that Lucy enjoyed going for meals at "gourmet restaurants". "Gourmet" means 'specialising in high-quality food'.

9. B
In line 19, Brian hopes that the trainers he has packed are suitable, so he has definitely packed his trainers.

10. D
Line 7 states that Lucy moved to Yorkshire "a couple of months ago". Line 10 states that "winter turned into spring". Therefore, Lucy moved to Yorkshire in the winter. Line 18 states that Brian left his luggage in the rack above his seat. Lines 21-22 state that Lucy's parents visited her last week. However, the text does not mention why Lucy moved to the countryside.

11. B
"fascinated" means 'mesmerised'.

12. D
"vibrant" means 'dynamic'.

Puzzles 4 — page 45
Word Snail

¹o	p	p	o	s	²e

Hidden Word: retreat

Cube Words
eagle   glance   legal   change
Nine letter word: **challenge**

Test 11 — pages 46-49

1. B
Line 15 states that it is a "quiet", moonlit night, and line 24 states that it is a starry night. Therefore it is clear and still.

2. D
Line 4 states that the horse is champing the grass of the "forest's ferny floor".

3. A
In line 3, the house remains in "silence", despite the Traveller knocking on the door. In line 13, the occupants of the house are described as "phantom listeners".

4. C
Line 9 states that "no one descended to the Traveller" after the second knock on the door.

5. B
Line 12 describes the Traveller as being "perplexed", which is another word for 'confused'.

6. B
Lines 21-22 mention how the Traveller feels the strange presence of the listeners, as though something can hear him.

7. D
Line 15 states that they "Stood listening" to the voice of the Traveller.

8. B
'crop' can mean 'to bite the top off a plant' and "turf" refers to the grass. Therefore, the horse is eating the grass.

9. C

In lines 27-28 the Traveller says "Tell them I came" and "That I kept my word". This suggests he made a promise to visit the house.

10. C

Line 5 states that the house has a turret, line 10 refers to the "leaf-fringed" window sills, and the stillness of the house is emphasised throughout the poem. However, a broken chimney is not mentioned.

11. C

'stir' means 'movement'. Therefore the listeners do not move.

12. B

The "sound of iron on stone" is the sound of the horse's hooves clattering on the stone ground. In line 33, the Traveller puts his foot in the "stirrup", which suggests he has mounted the horse and is about to ride away.

Test 12 — pages 50-53

1. D

The first paragraph states that Las Montañas del Fuego are on the "island of Lanzarote". You can infer that they are near Yaiza, as Yaiza is described as a "nearby village" (line 6).

2. A

Lines 1-4 describe the lava field that makes up the National Park. It is referred to as Las Montañas del Fuego because the area was formed by volcanic eruptions.

3. D

Lines 6-8 state that although nobody was hurt, farm land and villages were destroyed, leaving people with no homes or livelihoods.

4. B

Lines 10-11 state that the landscape remains "unchanged" because "low rainfall" has not eroded the rock.

5. C

Line 1 states that the original eruptions occurred in the 18th century (1730-1736); line 23 states that the most recent eruption happened in the 19th century (1824).

6. C

Lines 23-24 explain that the lack of recent eruptions has given tourists "peace of mind", suggesting that tourists are not worried that eruptions will happen again soon.

7. B

Lines 10-11 suggest that the land has remained relatively "unchanged" since the eruptions, so the area is well preserved. Line 12 states that the eruptions happened "recently".

8. D

Line 14 states that the area is home to lizards and birds. Lines 19-21 state how the extreme temperatures of the island are demonstrated. Line 9 states that the area is made up of "red, brown and grey rock". However, the text does not mention small trees growing in the lava field.

9. C

Lines 20-21 refer to the demonstration that converts water poured down a hole into a jet of steam.

10. B

"geothermal" means 'heat that is produced from within the earth itself'. "Geo" refers to the earth, and "thermal" refers to heat.

11. A

"expansive" means 'extensive'.

12. C

"commentary" is closest to 'narration' in the context of the passage.

Test 13 — pages 54-57

1. B

Line 8 states that Jo has a "burn and tear" in her dress. Meg tells Jo she should keep her back "out of sight" (line 10); this suggests that the damage is on the back of the dress.

2. D

Although lines 5-6 suggest Meg is 16, Jo's age is not clear from the text.

3. D

On lines 12-13 Jo says that she will "have to go without" her gloves. On lines 23-24 she suggests borrowing one of Meg's gloves so they can "each wear one good" glove. On line 22, Jo states that she can hold her gloves "crumpled up" in her hand. However, Jo doesn't suggest that she will buy a new pair of gloves.

4. A

On line 14, Meg tells Jo that she "must have gloves" or Meg will not go to the dance.

5. A

"Sloppy" best describes Jo. She has a burn and tear in her dress (line 8), she talks "with her mouth full" (line 4) and her gloves are "spoiled with lemonade" (line 12).

6. C

Line 1 states that "Mrs. Gardiner would be happy to see Miss March and Miss Josephine at a little dance". Therefore, Miss March has not invited the girls to the party.

7. A

The most likely meaning of "can't take any out" (line 9) is that Jo cannot remove the damaged fabric from her dress.

8. C

After hearing about the invitation to the party, Meg asks "what shall we wear?" (line 2) and is worried about her (and Jo's) appearance throughout the extract. This suggests that Meg sees the party as an opportunity to dress up.

9. B

The most likely meaning of "make them do" (line 21) is to 'manage with them'.

10. D

Lines 19-20 state that the gloves are "expensive", that Jo is "careless" with them, and that she "spoiled the others" and so won't get any more "this winter", suggesting the gloves were damaged recently. However, it is not mentioned whether Jo wears gloves often or not.

11. A

"decidedly" means 'decisively'.

12. B

"mortified" means 'embarrassed'.

Puzzles 5 — page 58

Spelling Treasures

A. 'Geoff purchased eleven **diffarent flavers** of ice cream.' — (different, flavours) — **(A, 2)**

B. 'Jennifer didn't like Nadya because she was constantly **growning** about something.' — (groaning) — **(B, 1)**

C. 'Nick's **granmother** had recently turned **ninty** years old' — (grandmother, ninety) — **(C, 2)**

D. 'Stuart was **definately surprized** to learn that **lightening** strikes the same place twice.' — (definitely, surprised, lightning) — **(D, 3)**

E. 'Kara **discurered** she had a fondness for caramel cookies.' — (discovered) — **(E, 1)**

F. 'Jackson certainly gave a very **convinceing performance**.' — (convincing, performance) — **(F, 2)**

G. 'Abigail had been incredibly **couragous** when she **confrunted** the menacing bully.' — (courageous, confronted) — **(G, 2)**

Hidden Message: "The treasure is buried in the cave."

Test 14 — pages 59-62

1. C
Lines 1-3 state that the duke sent his servants into town to "offer a vast reward to anyone who could restore his vision".

2. D
Line 6 states that Chang "set off to discover the lagoon".

3. C
Line 8 states that Chang had to rest because he was "Tired" (fatigued) and "thirsty" (dehydrated).

4. B
Line 3 states that Chang is "poor", so the "vast reward" is the most likely reason for Chang's journey. Although Chang might have wanted to discover a cure for blindness, he already knew about the fabled lagoon, so it's the reward which motivates him to undertake the journey.

5. B
Line 4 describes the text as "ancient", and because the book doesn't immediately reveal the location of the lagoon, it contains secrets.

6. A
Lines 17-18 state that the dashes had been joined together by "fork-shaped prints" (the bird's footprints) to reveal the location of the lagoon.

7. B
The bird completes the map after Chang untangles it from the snare, so the bird wants to thank Chang for helping it.

8. B
Line 14 states that Chang does not understand what the dashes mean; therefore, throwing his hands into the air can be seen as a sign of his frustration.

9. A
Bowing can be a sign of gratitude; therefore it is most likely that Chang bows to the bird to thank it for its help in finding the hidden lagoon.

10. C
Lines 23-24 state that the reason Chang is so wealthy is because he is showered with gifts.

11. D
"sporadically" means 'intermittently'.

12. C
"vial" means 'bottle'.

Test 15 — pages 63-66

1. D
Line 3 states that the Boston Tea Party took place in Massachusetts, a state in America.

2. C
Line 6 states that the Boston Tea Party was "a protest against the British government". 'Protest' is another word for 'revolt'.

3. D
Lines 8-9 state that the "EIC owed Britain money". This suggests that the EIC was in debt to Britain. Lines 9-10 state that Britain hoped that allowing changes to the price of tea would prevent the EIC from going bankrupt so they could repay their debts.

4. A
Lines 11-12 state that "Bostonians were unhappy about this interference in their trade".

5. B
Lines 15-16 state that some protestors "disguised themselves as Mohawks". Disguises are used to conceal identity, therefore, the protestors wanted to remain anonymous.

6. C
Line 6 describes the Boston Tea Party as a "protest". Throwing the tea into the harbour was a defiant act which formed part of the protest.

7. D
Line 17 states that each ship's cargo was "destroyed simultaneously", which means 'at the same time'. Boston has ports and a harbour so must be located on the coast. Lines 8-9 state that the "EIC owed Britain money", implying they had previously borrowed it. Although line 19 states that Britain closed the ports in Boston, it does not say for how long.

8. B
Lines 21-23 state that after the Boston Tea Party, coffee became the most popular hot drink as opposed to tea. Therefore, before 1773, tea would have been more popular than coffee amongst Americans.

9. D
The text states that "342 crates" (line 1), "40 000 kg" (line 4) and three shipments (line 13) of tea were dumped in the harbour. The protestors did not destroy £1 000 000 of tea.

10. A
Lines 19-20 state that the British government responded by "closing the ports in Boston", this meant that ships could not sail in or out.

11. C
Lines 18-19 state that the tea would have cost $ 1 000 000 or £650 000 today, but it does not state how much the tea was worth in 1773 when it was emptied into the harbour.

12.   B

Lines 24-25 state that American Independence occurred "three years" after the Boston Tea Party, which took place in 1773. This means America declared independence in 1776, which is in the 18th century.

Test 16 — pages 67-70

1.   A

Lines 1-2 state that the "village smithy" (workshop) stands "Under a spreading chestnut-tree".

2.   B

Describing the blacksmith's sweat as "honest" suggests that he works hard for a living.

3.   A

Line 12 states that the blacksmith "owes not any man". Therefore, as he doesn't have any debts, he cannot be working to pay them off.

4.   C

Lines 15-17 explain how the swinging of the blacksmith's sledge creates a similar beat to that of a church bell.

5.   A

The blacksmith's face is described as "like the tan" (line 8). This is another way of saying that the blacksmith's face is tanned.

6.   B

'Staring the world in the face' is a phrase that can mean 'having nothing to hide'. The blacksmith believes he has nothing to hide because he is a decent man.

7.   C

Although line 24 refers to "chaff" (husks of corn), they represent the burning sparks.

8.   B

Line 31 states that his daughter's voice sounds like "her mother's" — her mother would be the blacksmith's wife.

9.   B

When thinking about his wife in lines 33-36, the blacksmith sheds a tear.

10.   C

Lines 28-30 state that hearing his daughter's voice in the choir makes the blacksmith's "heart rejoice".

11.   B

"sledge" can mean 'hammer'.

12.   D

"toiling" means 'working'.

Puzzles 6 — page 71

Scene of the Crime

Mr. Potts committed the crime.
Mrs. Walker's watch was stolen on a "rainy Sunday morning" and so his garden would not need watering.

Riddle Me Timbers

One of the pirates carries his piece of treasure in the chest.

Test 17 — pages 72-75

1.   B

Line 2 states that Edith has lived through leap years; these years contain 366 days rather than 365, and account for the extra 25 days Edith has lived.

2.   C

Lines 3-4 state that Edith hopes her memoirs will be enjoyed by future generations of her family, who will read about her life.

3.   C

Edith was born in 1915, and married 19 years later (1934) "during the decade that the Second World War began". Therefore, the Second World War began in the 1930s.

4.   C

Lines 8-9 state that Edith became a receptionist in 1936. As she was married in 1934, Edith was married when she became a receptionist.

5.   D

Line 9 states that Edith became a receptionist in 1936, but gave it up in the 1940s. However, the text does not specify when during this decade Edith gave it up. Therefore, it is unclear from the text how long her career as a receptionist lasted.

6.   A

Lines 2-3 state that each day of Edith's life has made her who she is today.

7.   B

Line 6 states that Edith was married when she was 19. Since Edith is 99 at the time of writing, she has been married for 80 years.

8.   D

Lines 14-15 state that Edith has "five grandchildren" as well as "two great-grandchildren".

9.   C

Line 1 states that Edith turns 100 years old next week; therefore she is not 100 years old at the time of writing.

10.   A

Edith turns 100 on the 23rd October; therefore the month before was September. Line 18 states that Matthew's birthday was last month, so his birthday must be in September.

11.   D

Lines 22-23 state that Edith believes that failure to try (to not attempt something) is worse than failure itself.

12.   B

Lines 21-22 state that Edith hopes her family have rich lives that are full of experience.

Test 18 — pages 76-79

1.   C

Lines 5-6 state that Joseph Bell and Sherlock Holmes had "a similar process of deduction". Therefore, both were good at solving problems.

2.   A

Lines 7-8 state that Doyle "found it hard" to find a publisher for his book at first.

3.   D

Line 16 states that Doyle had an "exciting and varied life".

4. A

Line 10 states that Holmes became a "much-loved" character and that he was revived due to "public demand" (line 24). This suggests that he was very popular with readers.

5. A

Doyle was not a soldier in the Boer War but rather a medical doctor (line 19); he was a surgeon on a whaling ship rather than a captain (lines 16-17); and although he ran for parliament twice he was unsuccessful (line 18). Lines 4-5 state that Doyle was taught by a surgeon at university, and later worked as a "medical doctor" (line 19) which suggests that he studied medicine.

6. D

Holmes is described as "perceptive" (line 3). "Perceptive" is another word for 'insightful'.

7. B

Lines 13-14 state that Doyle increased his fees for the Holmes stories in an "attempt to curb his publisher's appetite". This is another way of saying 'stop demanding more stories'.

8. A

Line 12 states that the popularity of the Holmes stories "prevented him from pursuing other projects".

9. D

Line 15 states that Doyle "killed Holmes off".

10. D

Lines 23-24 state that Doyle brought Holmes back "due to public demand".

11. A

"portrayed" means 'depicted'.

12. A

"supposedly" means 'allegedly'.

Test 19 — pages 80-83

1. D

Line 1 states that John is "practical" and "has no patience with faith" or spiritual things.

2. C

Lines 10-11 state that John thinks there's "really nothing the matter" with his wife apart from "a slight hysterical tendency". This suggests that because his wife's illness isn't physical, he doesn't believe she is unwell.

3. B

On lines 4-6, the narrator suggests that the reason she does not get well faster might be because "John is a physician" (a doctor).

4. C

Line 14 implies that the narrator is unsure whether she takes phosphates or phosphites. However, she does not take both.

5. D

Lines 17-18 state that the narrator feels that work with excitement would do her good. Lines 22-23 suggest that the narrator feels that "more society" (the company of others) would do her good. However, it does not state that she believes time will improve her condition.

6. B

Lines 14-15 state that going on journeys to get exercise and fresh air are part of her treatment. However, line 23 states that John thinks the "worst thing" she can do is think about her condition.

7. A

Lines 4-5 suggest that writing her personal thoughts is a "great relief", and allows the narrator to say things she couldn't to a "living soul".

8. C

Lines 20-21 state that the narrator finds being "sly" about her writing (keeping it a secret) exhausting.

9. A

The narrator says "what can one do?" (line 8) and "what is one to do?" (line 11). This repetition emphasises that she is unable to change her situation, which suggests that she feels frustrated.

10. C

"scoffs" means 'mocks'.

11. B

"high standing" means 'well-regarded'.

12. B

The most likely meaning of "dead paper" (line 5) is that the paper is not alive, and therefore cannot tell anyone what the narrator has written.

Puzzles 7 — Page 84

Compound Clues

GOLDFISH, BACKACHE, GLOWWORM, SANDBOX, MOONLIGHT, KEYHOLES, BARCODE, STEPBROTHER, TIMELINE

Test 20 — pages 85-88

1. C

By not letting the weather "dampen their spirits", Ellis and Thea decide that they should have a good time.

2. A

Lines 7-8 state that the click of the camera causes the meerkats to "turn and face" Ellis with their "ears pricked". This suggests that the meerkats are alert. When the meerkats hear the second click, they "scurried" underground, suggesting that they are frightened.

3. C

"myriad" means 'a great number'. Therefore, the meerkats ran in a lots of different directions.

4. A

Lines 9-10 state that the duo "soon grew bored of looking at an empty, muddy enclosure" because the meerkats had not reappeared.

5. D

Lines 12-13 state that while they are on their way to the elephant enclosure, "Drizzle turned into showers, which turned into pelting rain". Therefore, they didn't go to the elephant enclosure because the weather gets worse.

6. C

Lines 15-16 describe Thea's map as "incomprehensible mush", suggesting that it's wet and impossible to read.

7. C

Lines 16-17 state that the lynx exhibit is an "indoor exhibit" and therefore it would "offer a brief respite from the elements".

8. B

Line 1 states that "Threatening black clouds had been scuttling across the sky all day" and that they "weren't surprised" (lines 2-3) when it started to rain.

9. C

Line 24 states that Ellis was "very keen" to join Thea when she suggested leaving the zoo early.

10. A

A "wash-out" is an event that has been ruined or cancelled because of heavy rainfall.

11. A

"persistent" means 'continual'.

12. B

"rousing" means 'inspiring'.

Test 21 — pages 89-92

1. C

Lines 3-4 state that "German planes aimed to destroy factories, ports and industrial centres" in British cities. Line 4 states that the "civilian population needed to brace itself against these attacks".

2. A

Line 1 states that the war began on 3rd September 1939. Line 7 states that children began to be evacuated on 1st September 1939 — two days before war was declared.

3. D

An 'exodus' is when lots of people leave somewhere at the same time. In the evacuation, lots of children moved out of the cities.

4. B

Lines 3-4 state that buildings like "factories, ports and industrial centres" were targets. Line 16 states that many children wrote letters home. Lines 12-13 explain how evacuees were taken in by families in village communities. However, despite being given name tags (line 10), the passage does not state that evacuees were given them by their parents.

5. A

Although line 17 states that some children found evacuation to be an ordeal, line 14 states that "Lots of children enjoyed life as an evacuee".

6. C

Lines 19-20 explain that the "Phoney War" was a period where there had been no bombing in Britain.

7. B

Lines 22-23 state that not all children were evacuated because the parents decided the family should "stick together".

8. D

The author would most likely summarise evacuation as a difficult but necessary process because the cities were unsafe. Logistically, evacuating 3.5 million people must have been difficult, and some evacuees would have found the process a difficult "ordeal" (line 17). Even with the "Phoney War", evacuation was necessary as children who had returned to the cities were evacuated again (line 21).

9. B

Line 25 states that in London many families sheltered in "underground stations".

10. C

Line 8 states that by the end of the war, "around 3.5 million people" had been evacuated.

11. C

"relishing" means 'savouring'.

12. B

"ordeal" means 'trial'.

Test 22 — pages 93-96

1. D

The phrase "tight grip" suggests that Jane is anxious about something. Line 1 states she has a "shaking hand" which suggests her fear of flying is the reason for her anxiety.

2. C

Lines 5-6 explain that Jane is braving the plane so that they can have a holiday together as a family.

3. D

Lines 4-5 state that Jane believes people who smile all the time "appeared insincere", so she does not always find smiles comforting.

4. A

Line 6 describes how Jane believes flying must be "tolerated".

5. C

Jane mutters the seat numbers under her breath because she is concentrating and thinking out loud.

6. B

Line 11 states that David has a "pristine leather suitcase", not a canvas one.

7. B

Line 9 states it is Michael's "first holiday abroad", but not that it is his first holiday ever; he has had "years of trips and vacations around the UK" (line 10).

8. D

Line 3 states that the family are going to Madrid. Line 9 states that they are going to see their foreign relatives. Line 12 states that they are going away for two weeks. However, the text does not mention how long the flight will last.

9. C

Lines 16-17 suggest that it is her children's enthusiasm that allows Jane to relax for just a moment.

10. A

Jane is at ease at the end of the passage — she thinks everything would be fine "as long as her children were with her" (lines 22-23).

11. A

"wary" means 'suspicious'.

12. B

"tense" means 'tight'.

Puzzles 8 — page 97

Cryptogram Conundrum

S H E R L O C K   H O L M E S —
14 8 4 10 15 3 23 19   8 3 15 13 4 14

T H E   G R E A T   D E T E C T I V E
26 8 4   20 10 4 21 26   11 4 26 4 23 26 18 1 4

A	B	C	D	E	F	G	H	I	J	K	L	M	N	O	P	Q	R	S	T	U	V	W	X	Y	Z
21		23	11	4		20	8	18			19	15	13		3		10	14	26		8				

Word Square

Answers include: ace, act, all, ate, cat, cue, cut,
eat, let, tea, call, cell, celt, clue, cull, cult, cute, lace,
late, lute, tale, tall, teal, tell, acute, actual

Nine letter word: "calculate"

Test 23 — pages 98-101

1. A
The snow is described as moving "stealthily" because it
falls "Silently" (line 7) and goes unnoticed until morning.

2. C
Lines 4-5 state that the snow hushed, deadened, muffled and
stifled the sounds of the town, making it quieter than usual.

3. A
Line 6 describes the snow as "floating" and moving
"lazily", line 9 describes it as moving "softly". These
adjectives imply that the snow fell slowly and gently.

4. C
Line 18 states that "the busy morning cries
came thin and spare". This suggests that there
are fewer people outside than normal.

5. B
The snow is described as "veiling" because
it covers and conceals everything.

6. C
Line 10 states that there was seven inches of snow,
therefore, the snowfall cannot have been patchy.

7. B
Line 13 states that people woke up earlier because
of the "unaccustomed brightness". This means they
woke because it was lighter than normal outside.

8. A
Line 15 states that people "marvelled" at the
snow, suggesting they were amazed by it.

9. C
Line 10 states "All night it fell"; the poem itself
describes the night and morning; the title of the poem
states that it took place in London; however, the
month the snowfall took place is not mentioned.

10. C
Lines 21-22 describe the schoolboys tasting the
snow, throwing snowballs and how the snow came up
to their knees. However, the passage does not refer to
the schoolboys shaking the snow from the trees.

11. C
"unaccustomed" means 'unfamiliar'.

12. D
"crevices" means 'gaps'.

Test 24 — pages 102-105

1. C
Lines 1-3 imply that Edward VI reigned "during
the sixteenth century", and so his reign must
have taken place during the 1500s.

2. B
Line 3 states that Christ's Hospital claims to have "the
oldest uniform that is still worn today". Although the
uniform looks very different to modern school uniforms,
lines 13-14 state that there are "a handful of schools
like Christ's Hospital" and so the appearance of its
uniform does not distinguish it from all other schools.

3. D
Line 4 states that the uniform has "Hardly altered in over
460 years". This means that the uniform is almost the
same as the one worn in the 1500s (sixteenth century).

4. C
Line 7 states that the school "welcomed 380 children"
when it first opened. Line 8 states that "Girls were
accepted, but they were in the minority". This minority
must have consisted of 189 girls or fewer, therefore
the school cannot have welcomed 190 girls.

5. A
Lines 7-9 explain that children from "poor London
families" were welcomed to Christ's Hospital and that
their uniforms were donated. Therefore, it can be
deduced that Christ's Hospital was a charity school.

6. C
Lines 11-13 state that in 1870, the Elementary Education
Act "made education in England and Wales more widely available
for children", and so "school uniforms became more widespread".

7. D
Lines 11-12 state that the Elementary Education Act
"made education in England and Wales more widely available
for children", allowing more students access to an education.

8. C
Lines 13-14 state that apart from schools like
Christ's Hospital, "most items on a school kit list will
look very similar". This suggests that the uniform
at Christ's Hospital is 'unconventional'.

9. D
Lines 17-19 state that uniforms can help "integrate pupils
from different economic backgrounds" because pupils from
less wealthy families cannot be judged "on their attire".

10. A
Lines 21-22 state that school uniforms could "prevent
expressions of individuality", stopping pupils from
expressing their personalities through their clothes.

11. D
"disobedience" is an act of defiance, and so defiant
pupils may loosen their ties or untuck their shirts.

12. B
"In the year it was founded" (line 7) pupils were supplied with
"the school's distinctive uniform" (line 9). Line 4 states that
the uniform has not been altered in over 460 years, which would
suggest that the school was most likely founded in the 1550s.

Test 25 — pages 106-109

1. C
Lines 3-4 describe the children as "ordinary suburban children". Therefore the children live on the edge of a town, as suburbs are located on the edges of a town or city.

2. B
Lines 18-19 state that the mother wrote poetry for the "christening of the new kittens". This suggests that the family owns cats.

3. D
A reason why they are called the railway children is not given in the passage.

4. D
Lines 9-10 state "Mothers never have favourites".

5. A
Lines 16-18 state that the mother writes stories and poetry and that she reads to her children, but it is not stated that she helps them write stories themselves.

6. C
Line 7 states that the house has "'every modern convenience'"; therefore it cannot be described as old-fashioned.

7. B
Line 14 describes the women as "dull ladies" because they are uninteresting.

8. C
Lines 18-20 describe how the mother writes poetry for the children's birthdays, the christening of new kittens and when the children were ill with the mumps; it is not mentioned that she writes poetry for the children after their tea, although she does read her stories aloud after tea.

9. C
Lines 9-12 state that Roberta is "the eldest" child, Peter is the middle child, and Phyllis is "the youngest". As there are only "three of them" (line 9), Peter cannot have two younger sisters.

10. D
"Creative" is the best word to describe the mother as she writes stories and poetry.

11. D
If somebody 'means well' then they have good intentions, but this does not mean they are always helpful.

12. B
"convenience" means 'amenity' in the context of the passage.

Puzzles 9 — page 110

Word Search Riddler

HOOCLS — school

NIMAEC — cinema

HOPS — shop

SEMUMU — museum

ONITATS — station

RAYBRLI — library

KAREBY — bakery

POTISLAH — hospital

Which building has the most stories? — Library

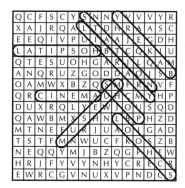

Test 26 — pages 111-114

1. D
Line 2 states that most people who know Archie "thought he was lonely". This suggests that they are worried he feels isolated.

2. A
Lines 8-9 state that "the thought of making new friends" made Archie "anxious". Therefore, Archie does not know the other children very well.

3. D
Lines 3-5 state that while Archie likes "having people to play with", he does not appreciate it when people try to force friends on him.

4. B
'To be happy in your own company' is 'to be comfortable being on your own'.

5. C
Line 6 describes the trip as "an attempt to encourage Archie to mingle with other children".

6. C
Lines 9-11 suggest that Archie is scared of the ride because when he looks at it his "stomached tightened", and the screams from the carriages make his "palms sweat".

7. B
Making new friends makes Archie feel "anxious" (line 9). The rollercoasters make Archie's "palms sweat" (line 11), and large crowds make him feel "overwhelmed" (line 17). But he's happy in his own company (lines 3-4).

8. B
In lines 15-16, Charlie tries to show how brave he is by boasting that he wants to sit "at the very front of the rollercoaster". However, line 23 states that Charlie "couldn't go through with it", which suggests he isn't as brave as he thinks he is.

9. B
Lines 7-8 state that the boys visited the theme park with "some children from the neighbourhood", therefore these children must live near Charlie and Archie.

10. D
Line 7 states that the visit to the theme park is "unsupervised", therefore the brothers' parents have not accompanied them.

11.   C

"raucous" means 'rowdy'.

12.   C

"anxious" means 'nervous'.

Test 27 — pages 115-118

1.   C

Line 1 states that Washoe is young in "the late 1960s" and line 13 states that Washoe passed away in 2007. Therefore she most likely lived between 1965 and 2007.

2.   D

Lines 23-24 state that some critics believed primates only used sign language "to obtain a food reward". Because of this, Washoe's family avoided teaching her around mealtimes to avoid "invalidating the study" (line 10), and so Washoe could not associate learning ASL with food rewards.

3.   A

Line 8-9 describes how Washoe's family only used ASL around her to create a "focused learning environment".

4.   C

Scientists stopped studying Washoe in approximately 1980. The project began in the late 1960s and lasted approximately 13 years; thus it would have ended around the late 1970s/early 1980s.

5.   B

Lines 14-15 state that Project Nim was created to "push the boundaries" and findings of Project Washoe even further.

6.   C

Washoe was alive between the 1960s (line 1) and 2007 (line 13). Line 16 states that Project Nim began in 1973. Therefore, Nim and Washoe must have been alive at the same time.

7.   B

Line 19 states that the Koko study is a "current study", suggesting that Koko is still learning new signs.

8.   B

Lines 2-3 state that "primates do not possess the physical capabilities for human speech". Therefore, primates are unable to master human speech.

9.   D

Lines 4-5 state that "as animals get older, our ability to acquire language tends to reduce". Therefore younger animals are better at acquiring language than older ones.

10.   C

Acquiring a language is a long process that spans the entire lifetime of an animal. We never stop learning language, so the projects need to span long periods of time to yield good results.

11.   A

Line 1 states that Washoe was a "female chimp". Therefore, she cannot have been the first gorilla to learn ASL.

12.   C

Lines 2-3 state that primates "do not possess the physical capabilities for human speech". Therefore Nim was taught ASL as he could perform hand gestures.

Test 28 — pages 119-122

1.   A

Line 21 states that the newspaper is just a "prop", so the elderly man is not actually reading it.

2.   D

Line 4 suggests that the narrator is suspicious of the "pretence" — he wants to know why the old man is pretending to read the paper.

3.   C

Nostalgia is related to memories. Therefore, the narrator's nostalgic love for spy thrillers from the 1960s is related to happy memories he has about them.

4.   C

On line 7, the narrator gives "retro gadgets" and "over-the-top acting" as highlights of spy thrillers from the 1960s.

5.   A

Line 9 states that "nobody would suspect" an elderly man of being a spy.

6.   C

Line 16 states that the narrator is suspicious, so it can be inferred that the narrator wants to see how the man will react.

7.   D

Line 22 states that the newspaper helps the elderly man "blend in".

8.   D

Lines 17-18 state that narrator wants an explanation for the elderly man's behaviour; this motivates him to ask for the newspaper.

9.   A

On line 23, the narrator feels his "face flush". This is a sign that he is ashamed of having bothered the elderly man.

10.   B

On line 25, the narrator realises that he needs to stop watching so many spy films, because they have clouded his judgement.

11.   B

"pretence" means 'deception'.

12.   C

"undoubtedly" means 'definitely'.

Puzzles 10 — page 123

Word Ladder

BELL to MAIL

BELL — BALL — MALL — MAIL
BELL — BALL — BAIL — MAIL

TINT to TALL

TINT — TILT — TILL — TALL

FLEW to SNOW

FLEW — FLOW — SLOW — SNOW
FLEW — SLEW — SLOW — SNOW

What Am I?

NOON

Chair

Test 29 — page 124-127

1.   A

Line 4 states that the children sit next to their parents so they can be "under supervision". Therefore their parents need to watch over them.

2.   C

Lines 1-2 state that it is "About half-past ten" in the "morning". Line 21 states that it is Sunday. Line 6 states that it is summer. However, the month of the year is not mentioned in the passage.

3.   D

Line 1 states that the church bell is "cracked", which means it is damaged.

4.   A

Line 8 refers to the mayor as one of the town's "unnecessaries". If something is unnecessary it is not needed.

5.   A

Line 10 states that Widow Douglas is "well-to-do", which is another way of saying 'wealthy'. Line 11 describes her as the "most hospitable", which means she is a good host.

6.   B

Lines 5-6 state that Tom is placed next to the aisle so that he is far away from the "seductive" summer scenes. The word "seductive" suggests that Tom finds the view distracting.

7.   D

Lines 16-17 state that the clerks stay in the vestibule until "the last girl had run their gauntlet". This suggests that they are watching the young ladies as they enter the church.

8.   A

The word "Model" is used in this context to refer to a perfect example. Willie Mufferson is model because he is "so good" (lines 19-20).

9.   C

Willie Mufferson looks after his mother like she is "cut glass" because he thinks she is fragile. Cut glass is very delicate and can be easily damaged or broken.

10.   B

In lines 22-23, the narrator says that Tom believes boys who have handkerchiefs are "snobs". A snob is someone who looks down on someone because they believe they are better.

11.   D

"lavish" means 'extravagant'.

12.   A

"simpering" means 'smirking'.

Test 30 — pages 128-131

1.   D

Line 2 states that the festival starts on a Friday, and line 3 states that it lasts for ten days. Therefore, Kinderzeche ends on a Sunday.

2.   C

Lines 3-4 state that Kinderzeche "honours the children of Dinkelsbühl".

3.   A

Line 6 states that the invasion took place in 1632. As line 7 states that the war began in 1618, it can be deduced that the attempt took place 14 years after the start of the war.

4.   C

Line 11 states that the Colonel's heart was "softened" by the gathering of the children, so he spared the town.

5.   A

Line 13 states that Kinderzeche has a "fixed format", which suggests that it never changes.

6.   C

The procession takes place four times. The first two times take place on each Sunday of the festival (line 14). There is another procession on the Monday in which school children take part (line 17). There is one more on the Tuesday, in which only children take part (line 18).

7.   A

Lines 16-17 state that on the Monday, school classes take part in the procession, and lines 17-18 state that on the Tuesday only children take part. There are also two Sunday processions (line 14) and "men, women and children" take part.

8.   B

Line 15 states that "men" and "women" take part in the procession, so adults must take part.

9.   A

Line 19 states that "Experienced onlookers" will find a good position to watch from. They will be experienced if they have been to Kinderzeche before.

10.   C

Line 20 states that onlookers may hand out "goodie bags" to those walking in the procession.

11.   A

The reason why the Swedish forces attacked the town is not mentioned in the text.

12.   C

Line 15 states that "four-legged friends" take part in the festival — this is another way of saying that animals take part. Line 22 states that some people dress up as "Colonel Sperreuth and his men". Line 16 states that the procession takes place to "the sound of brass instruments". Although lines 21-22 state that the Dinkelsbühl flag is "red and white" the design of the flag is not mentioned.

Test 31 — pages 132-135

1.   B

Lines 3-4 state that despite the poor conditions, the narrator slept well and it was "one of the best nights" he ever had.

2.   C

Line 3 states that position of the campsite is an "anxious one" because it is "five thousand feet above sea level", and therefore high up the mountain.

3.   A

Line 2 states that the "bed was hard, the shelter not very substantial". Therefore, "uncomfortable and barely sufficient" best describes the camp.

4.   A

Line 5 states that it is a cold morning — the air is described as "sharp" and "keen".

5.   C

Although the narrator mentions ponds on line 13, he does not see any; what he sees are actually lakes that just appear small.

6.   B

Lines 9-11 state that the view looks like a "raised map" because the narrator is high up and is looking down on the whole island.

7.   C

Lines 11-13 describe the landscape the narrator can see from the summit. Because he is so high up, everything appears a lot smaller than it actually is.

8.   A

Line 18 states that the narrator can "hardly tell" where the mountains end and the ocean waves start.

9.   D

Lines 19-21 describe how the narrator can marvel at the view without giddiness because he is becoming "accustomed" to the sights.

10.   A

Line 15 describes the mountains as "crested with sheets of snow". Therefore the island has snow-capped mountains.

11.   A

"innumerable" means 'countless'.

12.   B

"undulating" means 'wave-like'.

Puzzles 11 — page 136

Pet Puzzler

		AGE			TOY			PET		
		12	14	16	RED	BLUE	WHITE	CAT	DOG	RABBIT
NAME	MIKE	×	✓	×	✓	×	×	✓	×	×
	JOSH	✓	×	×	×	×	✓	×	×	✓
	CLARA	×	×	✓	×	✓	×	×	✓	×
PET	CAT	×	✓	×	✓	×	×			
	DOG	×	×	✓	×	✓	×			
	RABBIT	✓	×	×	×	×	✓			
TOY	RED	×	✓	×						
	BLUE	×	×	✓						
	WHITE	✓	×	×						

Mike is <u>14</u> years old, and bought a <u>red</u> toy for his <u>cat</u>.

Josh is <u>12</u> years old, and bought a <u>white</u> toy for his <u>rabbit</u>.

Clara is <u>16</u> years old, and bought a <u>blue</u> toy for her <u>dog</u>.

CLUE 2 – Mark that neither Clara nor the rabbit has the red toy. This does not reveal much at the moment but becomes useful later.

CLUE 3 – Mark that the dog has the blue toy. Clue 2 states that the rabbit does not have the red toy, thus it must have the white toy. This now means the cat must have the red toy.

CLUE 4 – Mark that Josh bought the white toy. Clue 2 states Clara did not buy the red toy, so she must have bought the blue toy. Thus, Mike must have bought the red toy.

Josh purchased the white toy, and the white toy belongs to the rabbit. Therefore, Josh adopted the rabbit. We can then do this for both Mike and Clara — Mike's red toy means he adopted the cat, and Clara's blue toy means she adopted the dog.

Using Clue 1 and this new knowledge, the youngest person adopted the rabbit. Josh adopted the rabbit, so he must be 12 years old (the youngest). The eldest person adopted a dog, so because Clara adopted a dog, she is 16 years old (the eldest). Therefore, Mike must be 14 years old.